SUMMER'S
LAB
A FIRST HANDS-ON
LOOK AT SCIENCE

Summer's Lab - Teacher Guide

First Edition 2020

https://elementalscience.com/collections/summers-lab

ISBN: 978-1-935614-71-5

For more copies write to:

Elemental Science
PO Box 79
Niceville, FL 32588
Email: support@elementalscience.com

Copyright Policy

A LETTER FROM THE AUTHOR

Dear Parent, Leader, or Teacher,

What follows is my attempt at making your student's first introduction to science a fun one! From this page on, you will be guided by Summer Beach, my favorite research scientist, who also happens to be a figment of an author's imagination. My co-author in the Sassafras Science series, Johnny Congo, created Summer as one of the main people to join the Sassafras Twins on their journey.

From the moment I "met" her, I knew she needed her own series. Summer is quite the quirky, bubbly scientist, who also happens to be a huge fan of sandwiches. And so, when I sat down to create a program from her, I knew that it had to be unique. Let's face it – what's more unique than a science sandwich!

I'll let Summer explain how this all fits together in the introduction, but before I go, I wanted to share a few quick tidbits about this program.

1. The science stories in the program are designed to start with silly sandwich tie-ins and end with very basic scientific facts in simple language. We don't go into a ton of detail because this is meant to be an interesting first look at science.
2. Feel free to switch around the units, but I would suggest that you leave the energy unit for last, since, in the very last week of that unit, Summer says goodbye to your students.
3. If you have any questions or comments about this program, please don't hesitate to contact us at support@elementalscience.com.

I hope that you and your students will enjoy visiting Summer's Lab as much as I enjoyed writing it!

Paige Hudson

TABLE OF CONTENTS

INTRODUCTION

A Tour of This Guide

Welcome to Summer's Lab!! I am Summer Beach, research scientist, Sassy-Sci supporter, and your host for this journey!

You may have heard about me through *The Sassafras Science Adventures* series, but if you haven't that is totally fine! I have known Cecil Sassafras, inventor of the invisible zip lines, for years, and I had a blast helping him teach his nephew, Blaine, and niece, Tracey, all about science. So when the twins (Blaine and Tracey) asked me to create an introduction to science, well . . . I have to admit I was floored!

Ulysses had to wave a toasted roast beef, cheddar cheese, tomato, and horseradish sandwich, which happens to be my favorite kind, under my nose just to get me to respond! I quickly recovered and Ulysses and I set to work. In case you don't know, Ulysses is my lab assistant, who also happens to be an arctic ground squirrel. He's quite the helpful mammal, although he does disappear each winter for hibernation, which can be a bit tricky if we are mid-project!

So now that you know a bit about me, let me tell you about your upcoming adventure. Ulysses and I are opening the doors to our lab to give you and your students a hands-on journey through science for the very first time. We designed this program to provide you with the tools you need to gently introduce your early elementary students to the wonderful world of science!!

Each week, you will be building a science sandwich that your students will want to gobble up! They will be learning basic facts about animals, humans, plants, weather, rocks, matter, and energy. And they will work on their observation skills as they encounter science face-to-face.

Let's take a closer look at each of the different sections!

The Science Sandwich

We will start our journey through science off with the basics of the sandwich. In other words, this section will contain all the information you will need to introduce the week's subject matter to your students. The week's sandwich basics, broken down into two sections:

- The Meat – This section contains a couple of paragraphs of introduction from Ulysses and me on the subject.
- The Bread – This section has several questions you can use with your students to make sure that they have picked up the key points, along with an optional coloring page and mini-book to add a bit of artisan flavor to the bread of your science sandwich!

You will start your week with this section and then add to the science sandwich you are building with the following sections.

Cheesy Additions

When you eat a sandwich without cheese, you just feel like it is missing something. The same is true for science without some hands-on projects. These demonstrations serve to bring the subject matter to life, just like a good sharp cheddar does for my favorite roast beef sandwich.

In the "Cheesy Additions" section, you and your students will be entering my lab and helping Ulysses and me out! We have included coordinating hands-on projects for you to use each week. These scientific demonstrations will help you lead your students to encounter science face-to-face! You will find the materials you need, the steps to you need to take to complete the demonstration, and an explanation.

These are meant to be guided by you and observed by the students. You can read more about scientific demonstrations here:

- Scientific Demonstrations vs. Experiments: https://elementalscience.com/blogs/news/89905795-scientific-demonstrations-or-experiments

The Mayo and More

Any good sandwich has "extras" like mayo, mustard, horseradish, tomatoes, or spinach. These additions add flavor and make the sandwich super yummy to eat. And that is exactly what the activities in this section will do for your science-learning time! You will find art projects, snack options, and extra science projects in this section. Each one is meant to add a bit of flavor and pizazz to your weekly science sandwich!

Listen while you eat

Ulysses and I have included pages from our favorite encyclopedia, the *DK Children's Encyclopedia*, as well as a list of optional library books that coordinate with the weekly topic. The books are just suggestions meant to be a springboard for a search at your local library if you want to add in some extra reading while you are munching on the science sandwich you have made.

Lunch Schedules

Ulysses and I have also included two scheduling options to make your job a bit easier. These will help you to see what you could cover each week. There is the list schedule option, which is a list schedule that shows you the essentials for a bare-bones snack, the keys to add for a full lunch, and the optional extras that will make a feast! And there is a grid schedule option for putting together your science sandwich in four 10–15 minute days, or you can smush two of the days together for two 20–30 minute sessions a week. You can choose to use these as your guide or create a completely different one that suits your needs better.

Student Resources

Before I go, I do need to tell you about two things the peeps on the Sassafras Science team have put together for your students.

- The Lab Manual - First, they have taken my ideas and turned them into a super-cute lab manual! It contains story sheets, coloring pages, demonstration sheets, and activity sheets. These pages allow your students to create a scrapbook-style lab manual with what they learned in this program.
- The Reference Notes - Second, the Sassafras Science peeps have create a series of reference sheets. These sheets contain the stories and a set of mini-books for the students to record what they have learned for that week. These are designed to be cut out and glued into the students' journals (or composition books) with lots of their doodles, notes, and thoughts around them. Alternatively, you can use these mini-books to create a lapbook.

Both of these student resources are sold separately, and you can use both, one, or neither of these. In other words, you don't have to have them to complete the program, though Ulysses and I do highly recommend them!

Final Thoughts

Ulysses and I hope that this program will spark your students' interests in learning more about science. We also hope that you enjoy this year of sandwich science from our lab! When the year is over, we highly recommend beginning *The Sassafras Science Adventures* series as a super-fun follow-up!

MATERIALS MASTER LIST

The following lists is for all the supplies need for the units, you may not need all of these depending upon which activities you choose to complete.

Animals Unit

Week	Hands-on Project Materials	Coordinating Activity Supplies
1	Frog Life Cycle Cards (Appendix pg. 227)	Sponge, Green paint, Apple, Marshmallows, Chocolate chips, 2 Green pompoms, 2 Wiggly eyes, Parmesean cheese container, Glue, 10 Small black pompoms, Tweezers
2	Cheerios, Pipe cleaner	Feathers, Paint, Different types of fruit, Pipe cleaners, Clothespin
3	Thermometer	Paint, Peanut butter, Powdered milk, Honey, Cocoa, Vanilla, Chopped nuts, Raisins, Mini M & M's, Reptile pictures, Glue
4	Plate, Several types of food (i.e., bread, cheese, crackers, honey, and fruit)	Construction paper, Glue, Scissors, Celery, Peanut butter, Raisins, Ants, Sand, Two jars (one large, one small)

Humans Unit

Week	Hands-on Project Materials	Coordinating Activity Supplies
1	At least 8 objects, some of which are living, some of which are not (Optional - 8 more objects)	Magazine pictures or colored pencils, goldfish crackers or gummy worms
2	Animal pictures, stuffed animals, or figurines, Magnifying glass	Old magazines with animal pictures or animal stickers, Animal crackers
3	Small ziploc baggie, Jell-O, Large grape, Kidney beans	Picture of a cell, Paint or various craft items, Pizza dough, Cheese (ricotta and mozzarella),Various toppings for cell parts
4	Large Ziploc bag, Bread, Coke	Pepper, Cucumber, Celery, Mushrooms, Carrots, Veggie dip, Colored pencils

Plants Unit

Week	Hands-on Project Materials	Coordinating Activity Supplies
1	Small pot, Bean seed, Potting soil, Water	Brown, green, and red tissue paper, Glue, Carrot sticks, Celery, Leaves, Tomatoes
2	A tulip, Razor or knife, Magnifying glass, Q-tip	Paint, Cake with flowers, A large White T-shirt (100% cotton), Cardboard, Flower, Masking Tape, Newspaper, Hammer
3	3 Bean seeds, Paper towel, Plastic baggie, Tape, Water	Red paint, Apples, Seeds and fruit with visible seeds, Glue, Paintbrush, Construction paper
4	Crayons, Paper	Pretzel Sticks, Green grapes, Paper Bags, Tissue Paper

Weather Unit

Week	Hands-on Project Materials	Coordinating Activity Supplies
1	Baking Dish (9 x 13 pan or similar), Foil, Clear plastic wrap, Graham crackers, Large marshmallows, Chocolate bar	White glue, Paintbrush, Several different colors of tissue paper (preferably yellow, orange and red)
2	Paper, Pencil	Light blue paint, Paintbrush, Glue, Cotton balls, 2 Eggs, Cream of tartar, Vanilla, Sugar
3	Clear glass jar, Jar lid or bowl, Ice cubes, Hot water	Eyedropper, Straw, Paper, Blue Jell-O, Cool Whip, String
4	Weather Stickers (Appendix pg. 231)	Magazine pictures, Bananas, Grapes, Strawberries, Raisins, Carrots, and Skewers, Paper, Colored Pencils

Rocks Unit

Week	Hands-on Project Materials	Coordinating Activity Supplies
1	Rocks, magnifying glass	Rocks, Paint, Butter, Graham cracker crumbs, Sweetened condensed milk, Chocolate chips, Peanut butter chips, Nuts
2	Globe or a topographical map	Colored paper, glue stick, Cheese, Air-dry clay, Paint

3	Toothpaste tube (full), Scissors, Empty yogurt container, Dirt	Paint, Hummus, Red pepper, White glue, Saline solution, Baking soda, White vinegar, Food coloring, Small bowl, Small cup
4	Air dry clay, Rubber insects or shells, Rolling pin	Paint, Several stamps or stencils with small plants or animals on them, Sugar cookie dough

Space Unit

Week	Hands-on Project Materials	Coordinating Activity Supplies
1	8 Sandwich-style cookies, Picture of the phases of the moon	Small balloon, Newspaper, Flour, Water, Salt, Paint, Picture of the moon, Bananas, Toothpicks, Melting chocolate
2	3 Balloons, Thick fabric (such as a woolen or fleece scarf), Thin fabric (such as a thin cotton T-shirt or pillowcase), Warm water	Markers, Picture of the student's face, Freeze-dried (or dehydrated) food, Toilet paper
3	Labeled picture of our solar system (Appendix pg. 232), Blank solar system template (Appendix pg. 233), Pencil	Black crayon or chalk pastel, Picture of the Milky Way galaxy, Silver glitter, Glue, Different types of fruit, Elastic string, Different kinds of beads
4	Foil, Toilet Paper Tube, Pin, Small flashlight, Constellation pictures (Appendix pg. 234), Rubber band, Sharpie marker	Gold star stickers, White crayon, Paper, Dark blue paint, Plain cupcakes, Blue and yellow frosting

Matter Unit

Week	Hands-on Project Materials	Coordinating Activity Supplies
1	4 Pipe cleaners, Round beads in three different colors (at least 3 of each color)	Paint, Sugar cookies, White icing, 3 Colors of M&M's
2	Various liquids and solids from around the house (such as ice, crayons, LEGO blocks, dish soap, water, or juice)	Magazines for pictures, Popsicles, 3 Balloons, Ice, Water
3	Small paper cup, Water, Plate	Food coloring, Water, Ice-cube tray, A variety of fruits and vegetables
4	Glass jar, Pipe cleaner, String, Pencil, Water, Borax	Epsom salts, Warm water, Glass, Food coloring, Paintbrush, 6 Cups, Eyedropper

Energy Unit

Week	Hands-on Project Materials	Coordinating Activity Supplies
1	Toy car, String (2 feet long), Tape	Paint, Marble, Plastic wrap, Several books, Cutting board, Different kinds of round fruits and vegetables, Several rubber bands, Measuring tape
2	An empty yogurt container, Wax paper, Rubber band, Salt, Sound makers (such as a radio, metal pot lid and a wooden spoon, etc.)	2 Paper plates, Paint, Tape, Beans, Rice Krispies cereal, Bowl, Milk, Toilet paper tube
3	A room with no windows, Pencil	Red, yellow, and blue paint, Paintbrush, Different colors of fruit, Flashlights
4	String, Magnet (bar or horseshoe), Variety of metal and non-metal objects	Paper, Thin cardboard, Paint, Several magnetic objects, Sugar cookie, Red and blue M&M's, Magnet

LIBRARY BOOK LIST

The following is a list of *optional* books that coordinate with the weekly topics. With the exception of the encyclopedia, these books are just suggestions meant to be a springboard for a search at your local library. All the books on this list are totally optional and not necessary to complete the program. Instead, they are here to serve as support for digging deeper into the weekly topics.

Optional Encyclopedia

- *DK Children's Encyclopedia*, 2017 Edition

Animals Unit

- *Frogs* by Gail Gibbons
- *National Geographic Readers: Frogs* by Elizabeth Carney
- *From Tadpole to Frog (Let's-Read-and-Find-Out Science 1)* by Wendy Pfeffer and Holly Keller
- *About Birds: A Guide for Children* by Cathryn Sill and John Sill
- *Fine Feathered Friends: All About Birds* (Cat in the Hat's Learning Library) by Tish Rabe
- *How Do Birds Find Their Way?* (Let's-Read-and-Find... Science 2) by Roma Gans and Paul Mirocha
- *The Magic School Bus Flies from the Nest* (Scholastic Reader, Level 2) by Joanna Cole and Carolyn Bracken
- *Miles and Miles of Reptiles: All About Reptiles (Cat in the Hat's Learning Library)* by Tish Rabe and Aristides Ruiz
- *Eye Wonder: Reptiles (Eye Wonder)* by Simon Holland
- *Reptiles (True Books : Animals)* by Melissa Stewart
- *Fun Facts About Snakes! (I Like Reptiles and Amphibians!)* by Carmen Bredeson
- *Are You an Ant? (Backyard Books)* by Judy Allen and Tudor Humphries
- *Hey, Little Ant* by Phillip M. Hoose and Hannah Hoose
- *The Life and Times of the Ant* by Charles Micucci
- *Ant Cities (Let's Read and Find Out Books)* by Arthur Dorros
- *Henry's Awful Mistake* by Robert M. Quackenbush
- *No Backbone! The World of Invertebrates* by Natalie Lunis

Humans Unit

- *Living Things and Nonliving Things: A Compare and Contrast Book* by Kevin Kurtz
- *What Is a Living Thing? (The Science of Living Things)* by Bobbie Kalman
- *What Do Living Things Need? (Science Readers)* by Elizabeth Austen
- *About Mammals: A Guide For Children* by Cathryn Sill and John Sill
- *Eye Wonder: Mammals* (Eye Wonder) by Sarah Walker

- *Is a Camel a Mammal?* (Cat in the Hat's Learning Library) by Tish Rabe and Jim Durk
- *Animals Called Mammals* (What Kind of Animal Is It?) by Bobbie Kalman and Kristina Lundblad
- *Cells: Building Blocks of Life (Lifeviews)* by Michael George
- *Cells, Tissues, and Organs (Sci-Hi: Life Science)* by Donna Latham
- *Enjoy Your Cells* by Fran Balkwill and Mic Rolph
- *Inside Your Outside: All About the Human Body (Cat in the Hat's Learning Library)* by Tish Rabe and Aristides Ruiz
- *Me and My Amazing Body* by Joan Sweeney and Annette Cable
- *The Magic School Bus Inside the Human Body* by Joanna Cole and Bruce Degen

Plants Unit

- *From Seed to Plant (Rookie Read-About Science) by Allan Fowler*
- *From Seed to Plant by Gail Gibbons*
- *The Reason for a Flower* (Ruth Heller's World of Nature) by Ruth Heller
- *Planting a Rainbow* by Lois Ehler
- *The Magic School Bus Plants Seeds: A Book About How Living Things Grow* by Joanna Cole
- *Seeds* by Ken Robbins
- *A Fruit Is a Suitcase for Seeds* by Jean Richards and Anca Hariton
- *Curious George Plants a Seed* (Curious George Early Readers) by H. A. Rey
- *A Seed Is Sleepy* by Dianna Hutts Aston and Sylvia Long
- *A Tree Is a Plant (Let's-Read-and-Find... Science)* by Clyde Robert Bulla and Stacey Schuett
- *From Pinecone to Pine Tree (Scholastic News Nonfiction Readers: How Things Grow)* by Ellen Weiss

Weather Unit

- *Hot and Bright: A Book about the Sun (Amazing Science: Exploring the Sky)* by Dana Meachen Rau and Denise Shea
- *A Sunny Day (First Step Nonfiction)* by Robin Nelson
- *The Sun: Our Nearest Star (Let's-Read-and-Find...)* by Franklyn M. Branley and Edward Miller
- *What Makes a Shadow? (Let's-Read-and-Find...)* by Clyde Robert Bulla and June Otani
- *Clouds (Let's-Read-and-Find... Science 1)* by Anne F. Rockwell and Frane Lessac
- *Little Cloud (Picture Puffins)* by Eric Carle
- *The Cloud Book* by Tomie dePaola
- *Down Comes the Rain (Let's-Read-And-Find... Science: Stage 2)* by Franklyn Mansfield Branley and James Graham Hale
- *Oh Say Can You Say What's the Weather Today?: All About Weather (Cat in the Hat's Learning Library)* by Tish Rabe and Aristides Ruiz
- *What Will the Weather Be? (Let's-Read-and-Find... Science 2)* by Lynda Dewitt and Carolyn

Croll

- *Watching the Seasons (Welcome Books)* by Edana Eckart
- *Sunshine Makes the Seasons (Let's-Read-and-Find... Science 2)* by Franklyn M. Branley and Michael Rex
- *Our Seasons* by Ranida T. Mckneally and Grace Lin

Rocks Unit

- *Let's Go Rock Collecting (Let'S-Read-And-Find... Science. Stage 2)* by Roma Gans and Holly Keller
- *Rocks: Hard, Soft, Smooth, and Rough (Amazing Science)* by Rosinsky, Natalie M, John and Matthew
- *If You Find a Rock* by Peggy Christian and Barbara Hirsch Lember
- *Mountains* by Seymour Simon
- *How Mountains Are Made (Let's-Read-and-Find... Science 2)* by Kathleen Weidner Zoehfeld and James Graham Hale
- *National Geographic Readers: Volcanoes!* by Anne Schreiber
- *Jump into Science: Volcano!* by Ellen J. Prager and Nancy Woodman
- *Volcanoes (Let's-Read-and-Find... Science 2)* by Franklyn M. Branley and Megan Lloyd
- *The Magic School Bus Blows Its Top: A Book About Volcanoes (Magic School Bus)* by Gail Herman and Bob Ostrom
- *Mary Anning: Fossil Hunter* by Sally M. Walker and Phyllis V. Saroff
- *Viewfinder: Fossils* by Douglas Palmer and Neil D. L. Clark
- *What Do You Know About Fossils? (20 Questions: Science)* by Suzanne Slade
- *Fossils Tell of Long Ago (Let's-Read-and-Find Out Science 2)* by Aliki

Space Unit

- *Faces of the Moon* by Bob Crelin and Leslie Evans
- *The Moon Book* by Gail Gibbons
- *The Moon Seems to Change (Let's-Read-and-Find Out Science 2)* by Franklyn M. Branley and Barbara and Ed Emberley
- *If You Decide to Go to the Moon* by Faith McNulty and Steven Kellogg
- *DK Readers L2: Astronaut: Living in Space* by Deborah Lock
- *Floating in Space (Let's-Read-and-Find... Science 2)* by Franklyn M. Branley and True Kelley*There's No Place Like Space: All About Our Solar System (Cat in the Hat's Learning Library)* by Tish Rabe and Aristides Ruiz
- *Scholastic Reader Level 2: Solar System* by Gregory Vogt
- *The Planets in Our Solar System (Let's-Read-and-Find Out Science)* by Franklyn M. Branley and Kevin O'Malley
- *Glow in the Dark Constellations*
- *The Sky Is Full of Stars (Let's-Read-and-Find... Science 2)* by Franklyn M. Branley and Felicia

Bond
- *The Big Dipper (Let's-Read-and-Find... Science 1)* by Franklyn M. Branley and Molly Coxe
- *Circus in the Sky (Kids)* by Nancy Guettier

Matter Unit

- *What Are Atoms? (Rookie Read-About Science)* by Lisa Trumbauer
- *Atoms and Molecules (Building Blocks of Matter)* by Richard and Louise Spilsbury
- *Atoms (Simply Science)* by Melissa Stewart
- *Solids, Liquids, and Gases (Rookie Read-About Science)* by Ginger Garrett
- *What Is the World Made Of? All About Solids, Liquids, and Gases (Let's-Read-and-Find Out Science, Stage 2)* by Kathleen Weidner Zoehfeld and Paul Meisel
- *Change It!: Solids, Liquids, Gases and You* by Adrienne Mason and Claudia Davila
- *Melting and Freezing: Matter (Science Readers: A Closer Look)* by Lisa Greathouse
- *Freezing and Melting (First Step Nonfiction)* by Robin Nelson
- *What's the Solution (Reading Essentials Discovering Science)* by Karen Lewitt Dunn
- *Mixing and Separating (Changing Materials)* by Chris Oxlade

Energy Unit

- *Ways Things Move (First Step Nonfiction)* by Robin Nelson
- *Energy in Motion (Rookie Read-About Science)* by Melissa Stewart
- *Move It!: Motion, Forces and You (Primary Physical Science)* by Adrienne Mason and Claudia Davila
- *Forces & Motion (Little Science Stars)* by Clint Twist
- *Sound Waves (Energy in Action)* by Ian F. Mahaney
- *Oscar and the Bat: A Book About Sound (Start with Science)* by Geoff Waring
- *Sounds All Around (Let's-Read-and-Find... Science 1)* by Wendy Pfeffer and Holly Keller
- *All about Sound (Rookie Read-About Science)* by Lisa Trumbauer
- *Light Is All Around Us (Let's-Read-and-Find-Out Science 2)* by Wendy Pfeffer and Paul Meisel
- *All About Light (Rookie Read-About Science)* by Lisa Trumbauer
- *The Magic School Bus: Gets A Bright Idea, The: A Book About Light* by Nancy White
- *All the Colors of the Rainbow (Rookie Read-About Science)* by Allan Fowler
- *Magnets (All Aboard Science Reader)* by Anne Schreiber and Adrian C. Sinnott
- *What Makes a Magnet? (Let's-Read-and-Find... Science 2)* by Franklyn M. Branley and True Kelley
- *Magnets: Pulling Together, Pushing Apart (Amazing Science)* by Natalie M. Boyd

Unit 1: Animals

Unit 1 At-A-Glance

Unit Purpose

This unit is your student's first look at the world of zoology. In this unit, the students will learn the basics of four of the major types of animals. (***Note** - Mammals will be addressed in the next unit.*)

Animal Topics

- ✓ Week 1: Amphibians
- ✓ Week 2: Birds
- ✓ Week 3: Reptiles
- ✓ Week 4: Insects

Supplies Needed

Week	Hands-on Project Materials	Coordinating Activity Supplies
1	Frog Life Cycle Cards (Appendix pg. 227)	Sponge, Green paint, Apple, Marshmallows, Chocolate chips, 2 Green pompoms, 2 Wiggly eyes, Parmesean cheese container, Glue, 10 Small black pompoms, Tweezers
2	Cheerios, Pipe cleaner	Feathers, Paint, Different types of fruit, Pipe cleaners, Clothespin
3	Thermometer	Paint, Peanut butter, Powdered milk, Honey, Cocoa, Vanilla, Chopped nuts, Raisins, Mini M & M's, Reptile pictures, Glue
4	Plate, Several types of food (i.e., bread, cheese, crackers, honey, and fruit)	Construction paper, Glue, Scissors, Celery, Peanut butter, Raisins, Ants, Sand, Two jars (one large, one small)

Week 1 Grid Schedule

Main Idea				
Amphibians, like frogs and salamanders, live the first part of their lives in water.				
Supplies Needed				
Hands-on Projects	Frog Life Cycle Cards (Appendix pg. 227)			
Coordinating Activities	Sponge, Green paint, Apple, Marshmallows, Chocolate chips, 2 Green pompoms, 2 Wiggly eyes, Parmesean cheese container, Glue, 10 Small black pompoms, Tweezers			
Weekly Schedule				
	Day 1	**Day 2**	**Day 3**	**Day 4**
Lunch Items	❑ Make the amphibian science sandwich - read the meat, discuss the bread, and color the page.*	❑ Add some cheese to your sandwich with the hands-on project: Frog Life Cycle.	❑ Read the *DK Children's Encyclopedia* pg. 15.*	❑ Add some mayo to your sandwich with the coordinating activity: Frog Prints.
Feast Fillers	❑ Choose one or more of the library books to read.	❑ Add some more flavor with the coordinating activity: Apple Frog.	❑ Add some more spice with the coordinating activity: Frog Feeding.	❑ Choose one or more of the library books to read.

** If you are short on time, these items will create a Bare-Bones Snack for your week.*

Week 1 List Schedule

Weekly Overview

Focus-of-the-Week

- Amphibians, like frogs and salamanders, live the first part of their lives in water.

Supplies Needed

	Hands-on Project Materials
Hands-on Project Materials	Frog Life Cycle Cards (Appendix pg. 227)
Coordinating Activity Supplies	Sponge, Green paint, Apple, Marshmallows, Chocolate chips, 2 Green pompoms, 2 Wiggly eyes, Parmesean cheese container, Glue, 10 Small black pompoms, Tweezers

Weekly Checklist

Bare-Bones Snack

- ❑ Make the amphibian science sandwich - read the meat, discuss the bread, and color the page.
- ❑ Add some cheese to your sandwich with the hands-on project: Frog Life Cycle.

Complete the Lunch

- ❑ Add some mayo to your sandwich with the coordinating activity: Frog Prints.
- ❑ Read the *DK Children's Encyclopedia* pg. 15.

Making it a Feast

- ❑ Add some more spice with the coordinating activity: Frog Feeding.
- ❑ Add some more flavor with the coordinating activity: Apple Frog.
- ❑ Choose one or more of the library books to read.

Week 1: Amphibians

The Science Sandwich

The Meat

Read the following introduction to the students (LM pg. 8, RN pg. 6):

Hi-ya! My name is Summer Beach, and I am super excited to be a part of your first look at science. I promise this is going to be more fun than eating a portabella mushroom burger topped with spinach, blue cheese, and balsamic dressing!

I wish that I could zip you all to my lab to teach you all about science, like we did for the Sassafras twins, Blaine and Tracey. But, alas, Ulysses and I aren't able to do so. Did I mention Ulysses S. Grant is my lab assistant yet? He's quite the smart little arctic ground squirrel and super helpful to have around.

But we are not here today to talk about me! We are here to learn about the amazing creatures known as amphibians! Before we begin, I must ask - have you ever played Froggy? Other than the fact that they are really good at hopping, what do you know about frogs? (Pause to give time for the students to answer.)

That was very interesting! Did you know that frogs are part of a group of vertebrates known as amphibians? The word amphibians means "two lives," and the creatures in this group literally have two lives!

Amphibians hatch from eggs and spend their early days swimming around in the water as fish-like larvae. Then, they grow legs and their tail disappears. The animals spend the rest of their lives as frogs, toads, or salamanders on land! We call this process metamorphosis.

Since amphibians begin life in the water, you can usually find them living in damp areas near water. They typically have smooth skin and are cold-blooded, which means they don't make their own heat.

Ok, it's your turn! Take a look at the pictures below. Can you point out which is the fish-like larval frog, the one that lives in the water? And which is the adult frog that lives on land?

The Bread

Discussion Questions

☐ Ask the students the following questions:

? Where do amphibians (frogs) live in the beginning of their lives?

? Where do adult amphibians (frogs) live?
? Do you remember what it means to be cold-blooded?

Written Assignments

- ☐ Have the students color the coloring page found on LM pg. 9.
- ☐ Have the students add what they have learned to the amphibians notes mini-book on RN pg. 7. Then, have them glue the mini-book into their journal.

Cheesy Additions

Scientific Demonstration - Frog Life Cycle

In this demonstration project, you and the students will go over the life cycle of a frog.

Materials Needed

- ✓ Frog Life Cycle Cards from Appendix pg. 227

Steps to Complete

1. Say to the students, "Today, Summer has asked us to record the life cycle of a frog. She has given us cards to use, and we have to place them in the right order on the frog life cycle sheet in our lab manual for her and Ulysses to review later. Let's get started!"
2. Give the students the frog life cycle pictures from Appendix pg. 227.
3. Have them color the pictures and then cut each one out.
4. Discuss with the students the order of the frog's life cycle. Have them place the pictures they cut out in the correct order on LM pg. 10 or in their journal. Then, glue the pictures down.

The Mayo and More

Coordinating Activities

- ✂ Art (Frog Prints) - Cut several frog-shapped feet out of a sponge. Have the students dip the sponges into green paint and hop their frogs all over the activity page found on LM pg. 11 or in their journal.
- ✂ Snack (Apple Frogs) - Make a cute apple frog snack with the students. You will need apple slices, marshmallows, and chocolate chips. Have the students follow the directions from this website:
  - http://teachlovegrow.blogspot.com/2011/09/f-week-apple-frog.html
- ✂ Activity (Fine-Motor Frog Feeding) - Glue two green pompoms close together on the top of a parmesean cheese container on the side that has the smaller holes. Glue two wiggly eyes on the pompoms. Once dry, give the froggy-container to your students. Have them feed the frog small black pompom flies using a pair of tweezers!

Listen While You Eat

Reading Assignment

- *DK Children's Encyclopedia* pg. 15 (Amphibians)

Book Suggestions

- *Frogs* by Gail Gibbons
- *National Geographic Readers: Frogs* by Elizabeth Carney
- *From Tadpole to Frog (Let's-Read-and-Find-Out Science 1)* by Wendy Pfeffer and Holly Keller

Week 1 Notes

Week 2 Grid Schedule

<table>
<tr><th colspan="5">Main Idea</th></tr>
<tr><td colspan="5">Birds have wings and feathers.</td></tr>
<tr><th colspan="5">Supplies Needed</th></tr>
<tr><td>Hands-on Projects</td><td colspan="4">Cheerios, Pipe cleaner</td></tr>
<tr><td>Coordinating Activities</td><td colspan="4">Feathers, Paint, Different types of fruit, Pipe cleaners, Clothespin</td></tr>
<tr><th colspan="5">Weekly Schedule</th></tr>
<tr><td></td><td>Day 1</td><td>Day 2</td><td>Day 3</td><td>Day 4</td></tr>
<tr><td>Lunch Items</td><td>❑ Make the bird science sandwich - read the meat, discuss the bread, and color the page.*</td><td>❑ Add some cheese to your sandwich with the hands-on project: Cheerio Bird Feeder.*</td><td>❑ Read the DK Children's Encyclopedia pg. 39.</td><td>❑ Add some mayo to your sandwich with the coordinating activity: Painting with Feathers.</td></tr>
<tr><td>Feast Fillers</td><td>❑ Choose one or more of the library books to read.</td><td>❑ Add some more flavor with the coordinating activity: Eat Like a Bird.</td><td>❑ Add some more spice with the coordinating activity: Catching Worms.</td><td>❑ Choose one or more of the library books to read.</td></tr>
</table>

** If you are short on time, these items will create a Bare-Bones Snack for your week.*

Week 2 List Schedule

Weekly Overview

Focus-of-the-Week

- Birds have wings and feathers.

Supplies Needed

	Hands-on Project Materials
Hands-on Project Materials	Cheerios, Pipe cleaner
Coordinating Activity Supplies	Feathers, Paint, Different types of fruit, Pipe cleaners, Clothespin

Weekly Checklist

Bare-Bones Snack

- ❑ Make the bird science sandwich - read the meat, discuss the bread, and color the page.
- ❑ Add some cheese to your sandwich with the hands-on project: Cheerio Bird Feeder.

Complete the Lunch

- ❑ Add some mayo to your sandwich with the coordinating activity: Painting with Feathers.
- ❑ Read the *DK Children's Encyclopedia* pg. 39.

Making it a Feast

- ❑ Add some more spice with the coordinating activity: Catching Worms.
- ❑ Add some more flavor with the coordinating activity: Eat Like a Bird.
- ❑ Choose one or more of the library books to read.

Week 2: Birds

The Science Sandwich

The Meat

Read the following introduction to the students (LM pg. 12, RN pg. 8):

Ulysses and I were recently on our first spring picnic, scarfing down our sandwiches – bagels with smoked salmon and capers, yumm-o – when we spotted some ptarmigan. The birds were moving in and out of the rocks, quietly searching for a meal of early spring willow buds.

I love to spot birds in Alaska in the spring because they are molting, which means they are losing their extra winter feathers. Ulysses and I like to gather these up to use for different projects and experiments in the lab!

Before I share with you a bit more about birds, why don't you tell me more about what you know about these animals? (Pause to give time for the students to answer.)

You are so smart!! Birds do have feathers covering their bodies, instead of the fur or hair that mammals have. The feathers help to keep them warm and help the bird to be able to fly. Birds also have wings instead of arms, which really gives them the advantage when it comes to flying.

Birds lay eggs and then sit on them for several weeks to keep them warm. Inside the egg, a baby bird develops, and when it is ready, it uses a special beak called an "egg-tooth" to break out! Mama bird feeds the baby partially digested food, a.k.a. puke, until it is big enough to fly out of the nest and find its own food. So glad that I am a mammal and my mom fed me milk instead!!

Ok, it is your turn! Can you find the wings and feathers on the eagle?

The Bread

Discussion Questions

- ☐ Ask the students the following questions:
  - **?** Where are the wings and feathers on the birds pictured?
  - **?** What do birds use their wings for? Their feathers for?
  - **?** Can you tell me something else you have learned about birds?

Written Assignment

- ☐ Have the students color the coloring page found on LM pg. 13.
- ☐ Have the students add what they have learned to the bird notes mini-book on RN pg. 9. Then, have them glue the mini-book into their journal.

Cheesy Additions

Scientific Demonstration - Cheerio Bird Feeder

In this demonstration project, you and the students will make a simple bird feeder, hang it outside, and observe any visitors you get.

Materials Needed

- ✓ Cheerios
- ✓ Pipe cleaner

Steps to Complete

1. Say to the students, "Today, Summer has asked us to make a bird feeder to hang outside the lab. We are going to help her observe some of the birds that live here. Then, we will record what we see in our lab manual for her and Ulysses to review later. Let's begin!"
2. Give the students a pipe cleaner and a bowl full of Cheerios.
3. Have them string the Cheerios onto the pipe cleaner.
4. Then, have the students shape the pipe cleaner into a ring and twist it together.
5. Head outside and hang their Cheerio bird feeder ring on a nearby branch, one that is visible from one of your windows.
6. Head back inside with the students. Over the next thirty minutes, observe and record any visitors the bird feeder gets on LM pg. 14 or in their journal.

Results and Explanation

The students should be able to observe several different types of birds coming to eat at their bird feeder. They should also observe the wings and feathers of the different birds.

The Mayo and More

Coordinating Activities

- ✂ Art (Painting with Feathers) - Have the students collect feathers from outside or buy feathers to use from the store. Have the students use the feathers as a paintbrush to paint on the activity page found on LM pg. 15 or in their journal.
- ✂ Snack (Eat Like A Bird) - Explain to the students that many birds eat fruit. Serve them various types of fruit, such as mangos and different types of berries, for snack.
- ✂ Activity (Catching Worms) - Cut up several pipe cleaners into worm-sized pieces. Give each of the students a clothespin and tell them that this is their beak. Then, have them collect as many worms as they can with their beaks!

Listen while you eat

Reading Assignment

- *DK Children's Encyclopedia* pg. 39 (Birds)

Book Suggestions

- *About Birds: A Guide for Children* by Cathryn Sill and John Sill
- *Fine Feathered Friends: All About Birds* (Cat in the Hat's Learning Library) by Tish Rabe
- *How Do Birds Find Their Way?* (Let's-Read-and-Find... Science 2) by Roma Gans and Paul Mirocha
- *The Magic School Bus Flies from the Nest* (Scholastic Reader, Level 2) by Joanna Cole and Carolyn Bracken

Week 2 Notes

Week 3 Grid Schedule

Main Idea	
Reptiles, like snakes and lizards, are cold-blooded.	
Supplies Needed	
Hands-on Projects	Thermometer
Coordinating Activities	Paint, Peanut butter, Powdered milk, Honey, Cocoa, Vanilla, Chopped nuts, Raisins, Mini M & M's, Reptile pictures, Glue

Weekly Schedule

	Day 1	Day 2	Day 3	Day 4
Lunch Items	❑ Make the reptile science sandwich - read the meat, discuss the bread, and color the page.*	❑ Add some cheese to your sandwich with the hands-on project: Reptilian Location.*	❑ Read the *DK Children's Encyclopedia* pg. 210.	❑ Add some mayo to your sandwich with the coordinating activity: Fingerprint Snake.
Feast Fillers	❑ Choose one or more of the library books to read.	❑ Add some more flavor with the coordinating activity: Chocolate Snake.	❑ Add some more spice with the coordinating activity: Reptile Collage.	❑ Choose one or more of the library books to read.

** If you are short on time, these items will create a Bare-Bones Snack for your week.*

Week 3 List Schedule

Weekly Overview

Focus-of-the-Week

- Reptiles, like snakes and lizards, are cold-blooded.

Supplies Needed

	Hands-on Project Materials
Hands-on Project Materials	Thermometer
Coordinating Activity Supplies	Paint, Peanut butter, Powdered milk, Honey, Cocoa, Vanilla, Chopped nuts, Raisins, Mini M & M's, Reptile pictures, Glue

Weekly Checklist

Bare-Bones Snack

- ❑ Make the reptile science sandwich - read the meat, discuss the bread, and color the page.
- ❑ Add some cheese to your sandwich with the hands-on project: Reptilian Location.

Complete the Lunch

- ❑ Add some mayo to your sandwich with the coordinating activity: Fingerprint Snake.
- ❑ Read the *DK Children's Encyclopedia* pg. 210.

Making it a Feast

- ❑ Add some more spice with the coordinating activity: Reptile Collage.
- ❑ Add some more flavor with the coordinating activity: Chocolate Snake.
- ❑ Choose one or more of the library books to read.

Week 3: Reptiles

The Science Sandwich

The Meat

Read the following introduction to the students (LM pg. 16, RN pg. 10):

A couple of years back, Ulysses and I were in Arizona checking out the Grand Canyon and the Petrified National Forest – which, by the way, totally rock! – when we had our very first smoked rattlesnake sandwich. I must confess that I am a bit afraid of snakes, so the thought of eating one didn't really rank high on my "Sandwiches-to-try" list. But I have to admit, it wasn't half bad!

I don't have any snake subs on the menu anytime soon, but I have developed a newfound respect and admiration for reptiles. Did you know that snakes were reptiles? Can you think of some other animals, like snakes, that reside in the reptiles class? (Pause to give time for the students to answer.)

Your responses do not cease to amaze Ulysses and me. We are so proud of you! Reptiles include animals like turtles, lizards, crocodiles, alligators, and snakes. These creatures are cold-blooded, just like the fish we chatted about a few weeks ago. On a sunny day, you can find them hanging out on logs or rocks, warming themselves up.

Reptiles are also covered in scales, instead of fur like mammals or feathers like birds. These scales help to protect and waterproof the reptile. And in the case of snakes, scales help them slither along the ground. The fastest snake in the world is the Black Mamba, but it is also one of the most venomous, so you definitely don't want to race this one!

Reptiles lay eggs, just like birds do. However, most of their eggs are soft and leathery, which makes it easier for the baby snakes to hatch. After all, they don't have beaks to use to crack out of the shell.

I could go on for hours, but instead I want to see your reptilian moves. Check out the reptile pics below and see if you can move just like they do! (Hint – Snakes slither across the ground, lizards walk on all fours, and turtles use their flippers to push across the land or through the water.)

The Bread

Discussion Questions

- ☐ Ask the students the following questions:
  - **?** Do you remember how reptiles keep themselves warm?
  - **?** What are reptiles covered with?

? Do reptiles lay eggs like birds do?

Written Assignment

- ☐ Have the students color the coloring page found on LM pg. 17.
- ☐ Have the students add what they have learned to the reptiles notes mini-book on RN pg. 11. Then, have them glue the mini-book into their journal.

Cheesy Additions

Scientific Demonstration - Reptilian Location

In this demonstration project, you and the students will see how temperature affects reptiles.

Materials Needed

✓ Thermometer

Steps to Complete

1. Say to the students, "Today, Summer has asked us to study how reptiles keep themselves warm. Remember that reptiles are cold-blooded, so they don't make their own heat. We are going to run a short test with a thermometer to see if a reptile's location changes its temperature. Then, we will record our findings in our lab manual for her and Ulysses to review later. Let's get started!"
2. Give the students a thermometer and read the temperature out to them.
3. Head outside and have the students place the thermometer in the sun.
4. After two minutes, read the temperature to them one more time.
5. Then, have the students place the thermometer in the shade.
6. After two minutes, read the temperature to them one more time.
7. Help the students record the temperature change on LM pg. 18 or in a chart they create in their journal.

Results and Explanation

The students should see that the temperature has increased rapidly when the thermometer was in the full sun and that it dropped significantly when the thermometer was in the shade. Share with the students that the thermometer is like a cold-blooded animal. The reptile's temperature changes very quickly whether they are in the sun or in the shade. So if a snake wants to warm up, he sits out in the sun. If he wants to cool off, he curls up in the shade.

The Mayo and More

Coordinating Activities

✂ Art (Fingerprint Snake) - Have the students make a fingerprint snake using the directions from the following website:

http://www.dltk-kids.com/crafts/miscellaneous/fingerprint_snake.htm

Have the students make their fingerprint snake on the activity page on LM pg. 19 or in their journal.

- Snack (Chocolate Snakes) - You will need ½ Cup Peanut Butter, ½ Cup Powdered Milk, ½ Cup Honey, 1 Tbsp Cocoa, ½ tsp Vanilla, ½ Cup Chopped Nuts, ½ Cup Raisins, and Mini M&M's. Combine the peanut butter and the powdered milk until blended. Stir in the honey, cocoa, vanilla, nuts, and raisins - in that order. Roll your mixture into small snake shapes. Add 2 mini M&M's for eyes, using the peanut butter to attach the candies. Place the snakes on wax paper on a cookie sheet and chill in the refrigerator until very firm.
- Activity (Reptile Collage) - Collect pictures of various types of reptiles. Have the students separate the pictures into categories that they choose. Some possibilities are to sort by color, by where the reptiles live, or by what they eat.

Listen While You Eat

Reading Assignment

- *DK Children's Encyclopedia* pg. 210 (Reptiles)

Book Suggestions

- *Miles and Miles of Reptiles: All About Reptiles (Cat in the Hat's Learning Library)* by Tish Rabe and Aristides Ruiz
- *Eye Wonder: Reptiles (Eye Wonder)* by Simon Holland
- *Reptiles (True Books : Animals)* by Melissa Stewart
- *Fun Facts About Snakes! (I Like Reptiles and Amphibians!)* by Carmen Bredeson

Week 3 Notes

Week 4 Grid Schedule

Main Idea	
✦ Insects, like ants, have six legs and a pair of antennae.	
Supplies Needed	
Hands-on Projects	Plate, Several types of food (i.e., bread, cheese, crackers, honey, and fruit)
Coordinating Activities	Construction paper, Glue, Scissors, Celery, Peanut butter, Raisins, Ants, Sand, Two jars (one large, one small)

Weekly Schedule

	Day 1	Day 2	Day 3	Day 4
Lunch Items	❑ Make the insect science sandwich - read the meat, discuss the bread, and color the page.*	❑ Add some cheese to your sandwich with the hands-on project: Attracting Ants.*	❑ Read the *DK Children's Encyclopedia* pg. 134.	❑ Add some mayo to your sandwich with the coordinating activity: Shape Insects.
Feast Fillers	❑ Choose one or more of the library books to read.	❑ Add some more flavor with the coordinating activity: Ants on a Log.	❑ Add some more spice with the coordinating activity: Ant Farm.	❑ Choose one or more of the library books to read.

** If you are short on time, these items will create a Bare-Bones Snack for your week.*

Week 4 List Schedule

Weekly Overview

Focus-of-the-Week

- Insects, like ants, have six legs and a pair of antennae.

Supplies Needed

	Hands-on Project Materials
Hands-on Project Materials	Plate, Several types of food (i.e., bread, cheese, crackers, honey, and fruit)
Coordinating Activity Supplies	Construction paper, Glue, Scissors, Celery, Peanut butter, Raisins, Ants, Sand, Two jars (one large, one small)

Weekly Checklist

Bare-Bones Snack

- ❑ Make the insect science sandwich - read the meat, discuss the bread, and color the page.
- ❑ Add some cheese to your sandwich with the hands-on project: Attracting Ants.

Complete the Lunch

- ❑ Add some mayo to your sandwich with the coordinating activity: Shape Insects.
- ❑ Read the *DK Children's Encyclopedia* pg. 134.

Making it a Feast

- ❑ Add some more spice with the coordinating activity: Ant Farm.
- ❑ Add some more flavor with the coordinating activity: Ants on a Log.
- ❑ Choose one or more of the library books to read.

Week 4: Insects

The Science Sandwich

The Meat

Read the following introduction to the students (LM pg. 20, RN pg. 12):

Creepy crawlies! That's what we are taking a look at this week!

I will be the first to admit that the thought of a pita pocket with spinach, tomatoes, and some honey-roasted ants makes me more than a little squeamish! But many people around the world eat bugs, like ants, locusts, and grasshoppers.

Ulysses says it is because insects are a great source or protein, but I suspect that it is because there are more insects on the Earth than any other creature! Insects live in every region and every habitat in the world.

Insects are part of a group of animals known as invertebrates. This means that they have do not have a backbone like fish and humans do. Can you think of some of the insects you can find in your area? (Pause to give time for the students to answer.)

Once again, your brilliance at this age does not disappoint! Now, I do have to point out that spiders are not insects. Those guys all have eight legs, and insects only have six legs.

Insects also have a pair of antennae and a body made of three parts. These parts are known as the head, or front part with the antennae; the thorax, or middle part; and the abdomen, or back part. Some insects also have wings, which always come in pairs, one on each side of the thorax.

OK, it is your turn . . . can you point out each insect's six legs and antennae?

The Bread

Discussion Questions

- ☐ Ask the students the following questions:
  - **?** Can you count the legs on the insects in front of us?
  - **?** Where are the antennae?
  - **?** Can you point out the three body parts (the head, thorax, and abdomen)?

Written Assignment

- ☐ Have the students color the coloring page found on LM pg. 21.
- ☐ Have the students add what they have learned to the insect notes mini-book on RN pg. 13. Then, have them glue the mini-book into their journal.

Cheesy Additions

Scientific Demonstration - Attracting Ants

In this demonstration project, you and the students will see what types of foods attract ants.

Materials Needed

- ✓ Plate
- ✓ Several different types of food (i.e., bread, cheese, crackers, honey, and fruit)

Steps to Complete

1. Say to the students, "Today, we are going to enter into Summer's Outdoor Lab to do a bit of research. We are going to help Summer and Ulysses discover which types of food attract ants and which do not. Then, we will record our findings in our lab manual for her and Ulysses to review later. We need to start by choosing different types of foods from our kitchen to test. Let's begin!"
2. Have the students choose several different types of food, such as bread, cheese, crackers, honey, and fruit. Have them set a small amount of their selection in different sections on a plate.
3. Take the students outside and find a place on the ground to set their plate where it can sit undisturbed for seveal hours.
4. Head back inside and wait forty to sixty minutes before heading back outside to check on the plate.
5. Have the students observe which foods the ants are surrounding and record the results on the chart on LM pg. 22 or on a chart they create in their journal.

Results and Explanation

The students should see that the ants were attract to food that had sugar, such as honey and fruit. This is because ants prefer the food with the highest amount and most digestable carbohydrate. Sugar is a type of carbohydrate that is easy for the ants to break down quickly. So the ants don't have a sweet tooth; they are merely going for the food sources with the most amounts of usable nutrients!

The Mayo and More

Coordinating Activities

- ✂ Art (Shape Insects) - Have the students make several different types of insects from shapes. You can use long thin rectangles for the legs and attenae, circles for the three parts of the body, and ovals or triangles for wings. Have the students glue their designs on the activity page found on LM pg. 23 or in their journal.
- ✂ Snack (Ants on a Log) - Make ants on a log with your students for snack using celery,

peanut butter, and raisins. Cut up a two to three inch piece of celery. Fill it with peanut butter and top it with ants, a.k.a. raisins!

- Activity (Ant Farm) - Have the students create and observe an ant farm. You can purchase a pre-made kit, or you can make your own using the directions from the following website:
  - http://www.artistshelpingchildren.org/kidscraftsactivitiesblog/2011/02/how-to-make-an-ant-farm-jar-and-watch-an-ant-colony-build-mazes/

Listen While You Eat

Reading Assignment

- *DK Children's Encyclopedia* pg. 134 (Insects)

Book Suggestions

- *Are You an Ant? (Backyard Books)* by Judy Allen and Tudor Humphries
- *Hey, Little Ant* by Phillip M. Hoose and Hannah Hoose
- *The Life and Times of the Ant* by Charles Micucci
- *Ant Cities (Let's Read and Find Out Books)* by Arthur Dorros
- *Henry's Awful Mistake* by Robert M. Quackenbush
- *No Backbone! The World of Invertebrates* by Natalie Lunis

Week 4 Notes

UNIT 2: HUMANS

Unit 2 At-A-Glance

Unit Purpose

This unit is your student's first look at the world of anatomy. In this unit, the students will learn the basics of living things, mammals, body cells, and the human body.

Human Topics

- ✓ Week 1: Living Things
- ✓ Week 2: Mammals
- ✓ Week 3: Body Cells
- ✓ Week 4: The Human Body

Supplies Needed

Week	Hands-on Project Materials	Coordinating Activity Supplies
1	At least 8 objects, some of which are living, some of which are not (Optional - 8 more objects)	Magazine pictures or colored pencils, goldfish crackers or gummy worms
2	Animal pictures, stuffed animals, or figurines, Magnifying glass	Old magazines with animal pictures or animal stickers, Animal crackers
3	Small ziploc baggie, Jell-O, Large grape, Kidney beans	Picture of a cell, Paint or various craft items, Pizza dough, Cheese (ricotta and mozzarella),Various toppings for cell parts
4	Large Ziploc bag, Bread, Coke	Pepper, Cucumber, Celery, Mushrooms, Carrots, Veggie dip, Colored pencils

Week 1 Grid Schedule

Main Idea	
A living thing can adapt, change, develop, grow, and reproduce.	
Supplies Needed	
Hands-on Projects	At least 8 objects, some of which are living, some of which are not (Optional - 8 more objects)
Coordinating Activities	Magazine pictures or colored pencils, goldfish crackers or gummy worms

Weekly Schedule

	Day 1	Day 2	Day 3	Day 4
Lunch Items	❑ Make the living things science sandwich - read the meat, discuss the bread, and color the page.*	❑ Add some cheese to your sandwich with the hands-on project: Living vs. Nonliving.*	❑ Choose one or more of the library books to read.	❑ Add some mayo to your sandwich with the coordinating activity: Life Collage.
Feast Fillers	❑ Choose one or more of the library books to read.	❑ Add some more flavor with the coordinating activity: Living Snack	❑ Add some more spice with the coordinating activity: Living Things Poem.	❑ Choose one or more of the library books to read.

** If you are short on time, this item will create a Bare-Bones Snack for your week.*

Week 1 List Schedule

Weekly Overview

Focus-of-the-Week

- A living thing can adapt, change, develop, grow, and reproduce.

Supplies Needed

	Hands-on Project Materials
Hands-on Project Materials	At least 8 objects, some of which are living, some of which are not (Optional - 8 more objects)
Coordinating Activity Supplies	Magazine pictures or colored pencils, goldfish crackers or gummy worms

Weekly Checklist

Bare-Bones Snack

- ❑ Make the living things science sandwich - read the meat, discuss the bread, and color the page.
- ❑ Add some cheese to your sandwich with the hands-on project: Living vs. Nonliving.

Complete the Lunch

- ❑ Add some mayo to your sandwich with the coordinating activity: Life Collage.
- ❑ Choose one or more of the library books to read.

Making it a Feast

- ❑ Add some more spice with the coordinating activity: Living Things Poem.
- ❑ Add some more flavor with the coordinating activity: Living Snack.
- ❑ Choose one or more of the library books to read.

Week 1: Living Things

The Science Sandwich

The Meat

Read the following introduction to the students (LM pg. 26, RN pg. 14):

Crunchy peanut butter and jelly on Wonder white bread - it always brings me back to childhood and the edible rocks we made! Delicious!! But we are not here to chat about rocks, we'll do that another time. Rocks are not living, and today we are here to discuss things that are living.

But before we do that, why don't you tell your teacher one thing that you know is living. (Pause to give time for the students to answer.)

Whew - you got that one right! All around us, we can find both living and nonliving things. And the way we tell which is which is that all living things have the characteristics of life.

This means that a living thing develops, changes, and grows. All living things reproduce to make exact copies of themselves or offspring that are similar. Living things are also able to move as they respond and adapt to their environments.

Humans are living things. I am a living thing. Ulysses is a living thing. Your teacher is a living thing. You are a living thing and so is your class pet!

On the other hand, nonliving things do not show the characteristics of life. They may appear to show one or more of the same characteristics, but they do not show them all. Rocks and peanut butter are examples of non-living things.

Take a look at the pics below and see if you can tell which is living and which is non-living!

The Bread

Discussion Questions

- ☐ Ask the students the following questions:
  - **?** What do all living things do?
  - **?** What makes something non-living?

Written Assignments

- ☐ Have the students color the coloring page found on LM pg. 27.
- ☐ Have the students add what they have learned to the living things notes mini-book on RN pg. 15. Then, have them glue the mini-book into their journal.

Cheesy Additions

Scientific Demonstration - Living vs. Nonliving

In this demonstration project, you and the students will investigate whether an object is living or non-living.

Materials Needed

✓ At least 8 objects, some of which are living, some of which are not (*If you cannot have actual living things, use pictures from books and magazines.*)

Steps to Complete

1. Set the objects or pictures out in a row in front of the students. Once you have the materials in a row, say to the students, "Summer already shared with us what makes something living or non-living. This week, she has asked us to look at a few more objects and scientifically determine if they are living by answering a set of questions. Then, we will record our findings in our lab manual for her and Ulysses to review later. Let's get started!"
2. Have the students examine each object, as you help them answer the following questions with yes or no:
   - **?** Does the object change, develop, or grow?
   - **?** Does the object reproduce?
   - **?** Does the object need food?
   - **?** Does it move?
   - **?** Does the object adapt or respond to what is around it?
3. Have them write the object name and the answers to the questions on the chart found on LM pg. 28 or have them add their observations to their journal.

Results and Explanation

The results of this demonstration will vary based on the objects you chose for the students to examine.

The Mayo and More

Coordinating Activities

✂ Art (Life Collage) - Have the students make a collage showing pictures of living things. Have the students cut out magazine pictures or draw their own pictures of things that are alive on the sheet. Have them use the activity sheet on LM pg. 29 or have the students make their collages in their journals.

✂ Snack (Living Snack) - Give the students a "living" snack of goldfish crackers or gummy worms!

✂ Activity (Living Things Poem) - Have the students work on memorizing the characteristics of life using the poem below:

A living thing must develop and grow
It must reproduce and adapt to know
A living thing has one, two, or more cells
Info around it sets off mission bells

You can simply repeat the lines each day and/or have the students copy the poem on a separate sheet of paper.

Listen while you eat

Reading Assignment

- There are no pages to read this week.

Book Suggestions

- *Living Things and Nonliving Things: A Compare and Contrast Book* by Kevin Kurtz
- *What Is a Living Thing? (The Science of Living Things)* by Bobbie Kalman
- *What Do Living Things Need? (Science Readers)* by Elizabeth Austen

Week 1 Notes

Week 2 Grid Schedule

Main Idea	
Mammals, like rabbits and humans, have fur or hair.	
Supplies Needed	
Hands-on Projects	Animal pictures, stuffed animals, or figurines, Magnifying glass
Coordinating Activities	Old magazines with animal pictures or animal stickers, Animal crackers

Weekly Schedule				
	Day 1	**Day 2**	**Day 3**	**Day 4**
Lunch Items	❑ Make the mammal science sandwich - read the meat, discuss the bread, and color the page.*	❑ Add some cheese to your sandwich with the hands-on project: Mammal Comparison.*	❑ Read the *DK Children's Encyclopedia* pg. 154.	❑ Add some mayo to your sandwich with the coordinating activity: Mammals Collage.
Feast Fillers	❑ Choose one or more of the library books to read.	❑ Add some more flavor with the coordinating activity: Animal Crackers.	❑ Add some more spice with the coordinating activity: Classification.	❑ Choose one or more of the library books to read.

** If you are short on time, these items will create a Bare-Bones Snack for your week.*

Week 2 List Schedule

Weekly Overview

Focus-of-the-Week

- Mammals, like rabbits and humans, have fur or hair.

Supplies Needed

	Hands-on Project Materials
Hands-on Project Materials	Animal pictures, stuffed animals, or figurines, Magnifying glass
Coordinating Activity Supplies	Old magazines with animal pictures or animal stickers, Animal crackers

Weekly Checklist

Bare-Bones Snack

- ❑ Make the mammal science sandwich - read the meat, discuss the bread, and color the page.
- ❑ Add some cheese to your sandwich with the hands-on project: Mammal Comparison.

Complete the Lunch

- ❑ Add some mayo to your sandwich with the coordinating activity: Mammals Collage.
- ❑ Read the *DK Children's Encyclopedia* pg. 154.

Making it a Feast

- ❑ Add some more spice with the coordinating activity: Classification.
- ❑ Add some more flavor with the coordinating activity: Animal Crackers.
- ❑ Choose one or more of the library books to read.

Week 2: Mammals

The Science Sandwich

The Meat

Read the following introduction to the students (LM pg. 30, RN pg. 16):

Mammals – this is the group of animals that you all will be most familiar with. Why, you ask? Because you are one of them! Did you know that humans are mammals? And so are arctic ground squirrels like Ulysses!

It turns out that you have more in common with your pet pooch than you think! Can you think of a few things that a pet dog, kitty cat, or lab-assistant squirrel have in common with you? (Pause to give time for the students to answer.)

Wow, those are some great ideas. Ulysses pointed out that he, the kitty, and your pooch all have tails. Thankfully, that is not one of the common features of mammals. Can you imagine your teachers running around with furry tails tagging along behind them?

Seriously, all mammals feed their young with milk. Momma rabbits, cats, dogs, squirrels, kangaroos, and humans provide this special, super-nutritious white liquid to their babies until they are old enough to eat their own food.

The other thing that all mammals have in common is that we are covered in fur or hair. And that fur or hair works hard to help keep us warm. You see mammals are warm-blooded, meaning that we trap and produce the heat we need to stay at just the right temperature.

Now, pull out your magnifying glass and see if you can count the number of hairs on your arm!

The Bread

Discussion Questions

- ☐ Ask the students the following questions:
  - ? What do all mammals have covering their bodies?
  - ? What do momma mammals feed their young?
  - ? What did you learn about mammals?

Written Assignments

- ☐ Have the students color the coloring page found on LM pg. 31.
- ☐ Have the students add what they have learned to the mammals notes mini-book on RN pg. 17. Then, have them glue the mini-book into their journal.

Cheesy Additions

Scientific Demonstration - Mammal Comparison

In this demonstration project, you and the students will do an observation and comparison of different kinds of mammals.

Materials Needed

- ✓ 3 Different animal pictures, stuffed animals, or figurines (Rabbits, lions, giraffes, pandas, or monkeys would all be good options.)
- ✓ Magnifying glass

Steps to Complete

1. Set the animals out in a line for the students to observe.
2. Say to the students, "Each of these animals are mammals, just like us! Today, we are going to enter into Summer's Lab and act as her assistants as we are going to create a chart comparing these animals to see how they are alike and how they are different. Then, we will record our findings in our lab manual for her and Ulysses to review later. Let's begin!"
3. Ask the students the following questions for each animal:
   - **?** Size - Is the animal big or small? Thin or wide?
   - **?** Skin Covering - What color is the animal? Does the animal have fur or hair covering its skin?
   - **?** Ears and Eyes - Does the animal have big or small ears? Big or small eyes?
   - **?** Arms and Legs - How many legs does the animal have? How many arms does the animal have? Does the animal have hands and feet like we do?
   - **?** Comparison - How is the animal like you? How is the animal different from you?
4. Have the students fill out the chart on the demonstration sheet found on LM pg. 32 with their answers or create their own chart with the answers in their journal.

Results and Explanation

The student should see that mammals are alike in some ways and very different in others.

The Mayo and More

Coordinating Activities

- ✂ Art (Mammals Collage) - Have the students cut out pictures of mammals from old magazines or use animal stickers that you have purchased and use them to make a mammal collage on LM pg. 33 or in their journal.
- ✂ Snack (Animal Crackers) - Have animal crackers for snack one day. As the students eat, talk about the different kinds of animals you find, what kind of hair, teeth, hands and noses the creatures have.

✂ Activity (Classification) - Collect pictures of various types of mammals. Have the students separate the animals into categories that they choose. You can have them sort by color, by teeth, or by where they live.

Listen While You Eat

Reading Assignment

- *DK Children's Encyclopedia* pg. 154 (Mammals)

Book Suggestions

- *About Mammals: A Guide For Children* by Cathryn Sill and John Sill
- *Eye Wonder: Mammals* (Eye Wonder) by Sarah Walker
- *Is a Camel a Mammal?* (Cat in the Hat's Learning Library) by Tish Rabe and Jim Durk
- *Animals Called Mammals* (What Kind of Animal Is It?) by Bobbie Kalman and Kristina Lundblad

Week 2 Notes

Week 3 Grid Schedule

Main Idea	
The cell is the basic building block of the body.	
Supplies Needed	
Hands-on Projects	Small ziploc baggie, Jell-O, Large grape, Kidney beans
Coordinating Activities	Picture of a cell, Paint or various craft items, Pizza dough, Cheese (ricotta and mozzarella), Various toppings for cell parts

Weekly Schedule

	Day 1	Day 2	Day 3	Day 4
Lunch Items	❑ Make the cell science sandwich - read the meat, discuss the bread, and color the page.*	❑ Add some cheese to your sandwich with the hands-on project: Jell-O Cell.*	❑ Read the *DK Children's Encyclopedia* pg. 41.	❑ Add some mayo to your sandwich with the coordinating activity: Crafty Cell
Feast Fillers	❑ Choose one or more of the library books to read.	❑ Add some more flavor with the coordinating activity: Edible Cell.	❑ Add some more spice with the coordinating activity: Cell Builder.	❑ Choose one or more of the library books to read.

** If you are short on time, these items will create a Bare-Bones Snack for your week.*

Week 3 List Schedule

Weekly Overview

Focus-of-the-Week

- The cell is the basic building block of the body.

Supplies Needed

	Hands-on Project Materials
Hands-on Project Materials	Small ziploc baggie, Jell-O, Large grape, Kidney beans
Coordinating Activity Supplies	Picture of a cell, Paint or various craft items, Pizza dough, Cheese (ricotta and mozzarella),Various toppings for cell parts

Weekly Checklist

Bare-Bones Snack

- ❑ Make the cell science sandwich - read the meat, discuss the bread, and color the page.
- ❑ Add some cheese to your sandwich with the hands-on project: Jell-O Cell.

Complete the Lunch

- ❑ Add some mayo to your sandwich with the coordinating activity: Crafty Cell.
- ❑ Read the *DK Children's Encyclopedia* pg. 41.

Making it a Feast

- ❑ Add some more spice with the coordinating activity: Cell Builder.
- ❑ Add some more flavor with the coordinating activity: Edible Cell.
- ❑ Choose one or more of the library books to read.

Week 3: Body Cells

The Science Sandwich

The Meat

Read the following introduction to the students (LM pg. 34, RN pg. 18):

Every time I make an olive loaf sandwich – I prefer mine on French bread with a few slices of tomato and a quick swipe of mayochup, which is a super delicious ketchup and mayonnaise spread.

But I digress, back to the olive loaf…

Every time I see a slice of olive loaf, it makes me think of cells, not the battery-kind or the room-kind, but the life-kind. Before I share a bit more about what I mean, what do you know about cells? (Pause to give time for the students to answer.)

That is fantastic! The cell is the basic building block of all living things, including our bodies.

Even though they are tiny, they are little powerhouses! Cells are responsible for all kinds of jobs. They can send messages, fight off germs, and turn food into energy.

All our body cells have a membrane that holds everything together. They are filled with gel-like liquid called cytoplasm. And nestled in the cytoplasm are different pieces, called organelles, that help the cell to do its job. One type of organelle, called mitochondria, looks like a kidney bean and helps to release energy.

At the center of the cell is the olive, I mean the nucleus! The nucleus acts as the control center for the cell. Okay, now that you know a bit about cells, can you, with the help of your teacher, point out some of the things we just discussed on the picture of the cell?

The Bread

Discussion Questions

- ☐ Ask the students the following questions:
  - ? What is a cell?
  - ? What can cells do?
  - ? Name one thing that is found inside a cell.

Written Assignment

- ☐ Have the students color the coloring page found on LM pg. 35.
- ☐ Have the students add what they have learned to the cell notes mini-book on RN pg. 19. Then, have them glue the mini-book into their journal.

Cheesy Additions

Scientific Demonstration - Jell-O Cell

In this demonstration project, you and the students will make a model of one of the cells in our body.

Materials Needed

- ✓ Small ziploc baggie
- ✓ Jell-O
- ✓ Large grape
- ✓ Kidney beans

Steps to Complete

1. Say to the students, "Today, Summer has asked us to make a model of a body cell. Our cell will have a baggie for a membrane, Jell-O for cytoplasm, kidney beans for mitochondria, and a grape at the center for a nucleus. Then, we will draw what we created in our lab manual for her and Ulysses to review later. Let's get started!"
2. Prepare the Jell-O according to the package directions. Have the students fill their baggies halfway full with the Jell-O mixture. Have them seal the baggie and place it in the fridge until it is soft set (about 30 minutes).
3. Once the Jell-O is soft-set, have the students open the baggie and insert the grape in the center for the nucleus of the cell.
4. Then have them place several kidney beans in the Jell-O to represent mitochondria.
5. Have the students seal up the baggie so they can observe the body cell and record what they did on LM pg. 36 or in their journal.

Results and Explanation

The students should have a model of a cell that they can manipulate and observe.

The Mayo and More

Coordinating Activities

- ✂ Art (Crafty cell) - Have the students create a cell out of craft materials. You will need a picture of a cell, plus paint to create the different organelles or various craft items, like sequins, pom-poms, feathers, and so on. Let the students look at a picture of a cell and then let their imaginations loose as they create a crafty version of the cell. Have the students use the circle on LM pg. 37 for their cell or have them draw a circle to use in their journal.
- ✂ Snack (Edible Cell) - Make a cell that you can eat! You can follow the directions on this post for a cell calzone:

- https://elementalscience.com/blogs/science-activities/edible-cell-calzone-anatomy-project
- ACTIVITY (CELL BUILDER) - Have the students build their own cells with this on-line cell builder:
  - https://www.sciencegamecenter.org/games/build-a-cell

LISTEN WHILE YOU EAT

READING ASSIGNMENT

- *DK Children's Encyclopedia* pg. 41 (Body Cells)

BOOK SUGGESTIONS

- *Cells: Building Blocks of Life (Lifeviews)* by Michael George
- *Cells, Tissues, and Organs (Sci-Hi: Life Science)* by Donna Latham
- *Enjoy Your Cells* by Fran Balkwill and Mic Rolph

Week 3 Notes

Week 4 Grid Schedule

Main Idea	
The human body is made up of systems that have organs, each with their own job.	
Supplies Needed	
Hands-on Projects	Large Ziploc bag, Bread, Coke
Coordinating Activities	Pepper, Cucumber, Celery, Mushrooms, Carrots, Veggie dip, Colored pencils

Weekly Schedule

	Day 1	Day 2	Day 3	Day 4
Lunch Items	❑ Make the human body science sandwich - read the meat, discuss the bread, and color the page.*	❑ Add some cheese to your sandwich with the hands-on project: Model Stomach.*	❑ Read the *DK Children's Encyclopedia* pg. 130.	❑ Add some mayo to your sandwich with the coordinating activity: Body Organization.
Feast Fillers	❑ Choose one or more of the library books to read.	❑ Add some more flavor with the coordinating activity: Veggie Body.	❑ Add some more spice with the coordinating activity: Body Systems Booklet.	❑ Choose one or more of the library books to read.

** If you are short on time, these items will create a Bare-Bones Snack for your week.*

Week 4 List Schedule

Weekly Overview

Focus-of-the-Week

- The human body is made up of systems that have organs, each with their own job.

Supplies Needed

	Hands-on Project Materials
Hands-on Project Materials	Large Ziploc bag, Bread, Coke
Coordinating Activity Supplies	Pepper, Cucumber, Celery, Mushrooms, Carrots, Veggie dip, Colored pencils

Weekly Checklist

Bare-Bones Snack

- ❑ Make the human body science sandwich - read the meat, discuss the bread, and color the page.
- ❑ Add some cheese to your sandwich with the hands-on project: Model Stomach.

Complete the Lunch

- ❑ Add some mayo to your sandwich with the coordinating activity: Body Organization.
- ❑ Read the *DK Children's Encyclopedia* pg. 130.

Making it a Feast

- ❑ Add some more spice with the coordinating activity: Body Systems Booklet.
- ❑ Add some more flavor with the coordinating activity: Veggie Body.
- ❑ Choose one or more of the library books to read.

Week 4: The Human Body

The Science Sandwich

The Meat

Read the following introduction to the students (LM pg. 38, RN pg. 20):

A good sandwich is composed of several parts that work together to provide a superb dining experience. Take the humble shrimp po-boy – tiny, crunchy, but juicy shrimp mix with cool lettuce, flavorful remoulade sauce, and the perfect crisp, but soft, French bread.

Each part of the sandwich plays a role in making the shrimp po-boy irresistible to Ulysses and me! How does this relate to the human body? I'll get to that in a moment, but before I do, what do you know about the human body? (Pause to give time for the students to answer.)

Great answers! Let's chat about this sandwich-body relationship.

The human body, just like a good sandwich, is composed of many systems. These systems have structures, called organs, each with their own job. And these organs are made from tissues, which are composed of the very cells we chatted about last week!

Let's look at the digestive system, which is responsible for breaking down your food into bits your body can use for energy. Your teeth, esophagus, stomach, small intestines, and large intestines all work to break down food and absorb nutrients as the morsels you eat pass through these organs. They work together in a system, along with a few other organs, to turn those sandwiches into fuel for your body!

Okay, now it's your turn – take a moment to marvel at and observe the largest organ on your body, your skin! The skin, along with the hair, nails, and several glands, are parts of the integumentary system.

The Bread

Discussion Questions

- [ ] Ask the students the following questions:
  - ? What is the human body made up of?
  - ? What is an organ?
  - ? What is the largest organ in the human body?

Written Assignment

- [ ] Have the students color the coloring page found on LM pg. 39.
- [ ] Have the students add what they have learned to the human body notes mini-book on RN pg. 21. Then, have them glue the mini-book into their journal.

Cheesy Additions

Scientific Demonstration - Model Stomach

In this demonstration project, you and the students will make a model of the human body organ, the stomach.

Materials Needed

- ✓ Large ziploc bag
- ✓ Bread
- ✓ Coke

Steps to Complete

1. Say to the students, "Today, Summer has asked us to make a quick model of one of the digestive organs, the stomach. Then, we are going to use that model to take a look at how our stomach digests food. Then, we will take a picture and record our observations in our lab manual for her and Ulysses to review later. Let's get started!"
2. Hand the students a large ziploc baggie and tell them that this is their model stomach.
3. Have them open the bag and add several pieces of bread. Have them mush up the bread with their hands, simulating what happens when they chew up the bread.
4. Then, have them add one cup of coke to simulate stomach acid. Continue to squeeze and shake the bag around to see what happens to the bread.
5. Help the students record what happened on LM pg. 40 or in their journal.

Results and Explanation

The students should see that the bread breaks down into a pulp. In the stomach, the same thing happens to our food.

The Mayo and More

Coordinating Activities

- ✂ Art (Body Organization) - Have the students create a poster that shows the organization of the body (e.g., cells form tissue, tissue forms organs, organs form systems, systems work together to keep the body functioning). You can use the Body Organization Cards found in the Appendix of the guide on pg. 228. Have the students glue the pictures in the right order on LM pg. 41 or in their journal.
- ✂ Snack (Veggie Body) - Use slices of a pepper, cucumber, celery, mushrooms, and carrots to create the shape of a skeleton with a bowl of dip as the head of the body. Then, serve the Veggie Body for snack! (*Note - For a visual reference, check out this post: http://feedingfourlittlemonkeys.blogspot.com/2008/10/veggie-skeleton.html*)
- ✂ Activity (Body Systems Booklet) - Have the students make a booklet with all the body

systems. You can create your own using the information from the reading assignment or you can download one for free from here:

- https://www.totschooling.net/2016/10/my-body-systems-science-booklet.html

Listen while you eat

Reading Assignment

- *DK Children's Encyclopedia* pg. 130 (Human Body)

Book Suggestions

- *Inside Your Outside: All About the Human Body (Cat in the Hat's Learning Library)* by Tish Rabe and Aristides Ruiz
- *Me and My Amazing Body* by Joan Sweeney and Annette Cable
- *The Magic School Bus Inside the Human Body* by Joanna Cole and Bruce Degen

Week 4 Notes

SUMMER'S LAB
UNIT 3: PLANTS

Unit 3 At-A-Glance

Unit Purpose

This unit is your student's first look at the world of botany. In this unit, the students will learn the basics of plants and their parts.

Plant Topics

- ✓ Week 1: Plants
- ✓ Week 2: Flowers
- ✓ Week 3: Seeds
- ✓ Week 4: Trees

Supplies Needed

Week	Hands-on Project Materials	Coordinating Activity Supplies
1	Small pot, Bean seed, Potting soil, Water	Brown, green, and red tissue paper, Glue, Carrot sticks, Celery, Leaves, Tomatoes
2	A tulip, Razor or knife, Magnifying glass, Q-tip	Paint, Cake with flowers, A large White T-shirt (100% cotton), Cardboard, Flower, Masking Tape, Newspaper, Hammer
3	3 Bean seeds, Paper towel, Plastic baggie, Tape, Water	Red paint, Apples, Seeds and fruit with visible seeds, Glue, Paintbrush, Construction paper
4	Crayons, Paper	Pretzel Sticks, Green grapes, Paper Bags, Tissue Paper

Week 1 Grid Schedule

Main Idea	
Plants grow toward the light.	

Supplies Needed	
Hands-on Projects	Small pot, Bean seed, Potting soil, Water
Coordinating Activities	Brown, green, and red tissue paper, Glue, Carrot sticks, Celery, Leaves, Tomatoes

Weekly Schedule

	Day 1	Day 2	Day 3	Day 4
Lunch Items	❑ Make the plant science sandwich - read the meat, discuss the bread, and color the page.*	❑ Add some cheese to your sandwich with the hands-on project: Plant Growth.*	❑ Read the *DK Children's Encyclopedia* pg. 194.	❑ Add some mayo to your sandwich with the coordinating activity: Mosaic Plant.
Feast Fillers	❑ Choose one or more of the library books to read.	❑ Add some more flavor with the coordinating activity: Plants We Eat.	❑ Add some more spice with the coordinating activity: Plant Growth Video.	❑ Choose one or more of the library books to read.

** If you are short on time, this item will create a Bare-Bones Snack for your week.*

Week I List Schedule

Weekly Overview

Focus-of-the-Week

- Plants grow toward the light.

Supplies Needed

	Hands-on Project Materials
Hands-on Project Materials	Small pot, Bean seed, Potting soil, Water
Coordinating Activity Supplies	Brown, green, and red tissue paper, Glue, Carrot sticks, Celery, Leaves, Tomatoes

Weekly Checklist

Bare-Bones Snack

- ❑ Make the plant science sandwich - read the meat, discuss the bread, and color the page.
- ❑ Add some cheese to your sandwich with the hands-on project: Plant Growth.

Complete the Lunch

- ❑ Add some mayo to your sandwich with the coordinating activity: Mosaic Plant.
- ❑ Read the *DK Children's Encyclopedia* pg. 194.

Making it a Feast

- ❑ Add some more spice with the coordinating activity: Plant Growth Video.
- ❑ Add some more flavor with the coordinating activity: Plants We Eat.
- ❑ Choose one or more of the library books to read.

Week 1: Plants

The Science Sandwich

The Meat

Read the following introduction to the students (LM pg. 44, RN pg. 22):

Ulysses and I love plants, but since the area around our lab is often covered in snow . . . I haven't yet mentioned that our lab is underground in Alaska, have I?

Well it is. And because of that, we have an indoor greenhouse with grow lights to test out our plant experiments.

Plants are super important for sustaining life on Earth, but before we get to that – let me ask you a question. What do you know about plants? (Pause to give time for the students to answer.)

Wowzers – we haven't even started learning about plants and you already know all that! Super impressive! Plants use light, water, and air to make food. We call the process plants use to make food photosynthesis. Which basically means "light" is "putting together." Kinda funny, eh?

Plants use light from the sun as energy. And a little substance inside the leaves, called chlorophyll, takes the energy and changes the nutrients the plant absorb into food it can use to grow. The chlorophyll is also the part that give the leaf its green color.

So, since plants need light to make food, they typically grow toward the light. But the super cool thing about plants is that in the process of creating the food they need, these plants give off oxygen, which we need to survive!

We are going to spend the next few weeks going over the different parts of the plant, so for now I will just leave you with a picture of one of my favorites, the crocus!

The Bread

Discussion Questions

- ☐ Ask the students the following questions:
  - **?** Where do plants like to grow toward?
  - **?** What makes plants green?

Written Assignments

- ☐ Have the students color the coloring page found on LM pg. 45.
- ☐ Have the students add what they have learned to the plants notes mini-book on RN pg. 23. Then, have them glue the mini-book into their journal.

Cheesy Additions

Scientific Demonstration - Plant Growth

In this demonstration project, you and the students will observe and chart the growth of a plant. This project will last the remainder of the unit.

Materials Needed

- ✓ Small pot
- ✓ Bean seed
- ✓ Potting soil
- ✓ Water

Steps to Complete

1. Gather up the supplies needed to begin this project.
2. Say to the students, "Summer has asked us to begin a six week long project where will be observing the growth of a bean seed. Today we are going to plant our seed, water it, and watch what happens! At the end of each week we are going to measure how much our bean plant has grown and record it on a chart for Summer and Ulysses."
3. Fill the pot with soil. Then, have the students make an indention in the soil large enough for the seed.
4. Place the seed in the hole and cover it with dirt. Give the seed a bit of water and then set it in a safe place where it can sit undisturbed.
5. Over the rest of the unit, have the students check their bean seed each day and water it if the soil appears dry. At the end of each week, have them measure the plant's growth and fill out the demonstration sheet found on LM pg. 46 or in their journal.

Results and Explanation

The students should see that each week the plant continues to grow straight up and toward the light.

The Mayo and More

Coordinating Activities

- ✂ Art (Mosaic Plant) - Have the students cut up squares of tissue paper in brown for the stem, green for the leaves, and red for the fruit and flower. Have the students ball up the paper and glue it onto the plant pictures on the sheet found on LM pg. 47 or in their journal. When they are finished, have the students draw the sun above the flower to remind them that plants grow toward the light.
- ✂ Snack (Plants We Eat) - Explain to the students that we eat many different types of plants and different parts of the plants every day. These foods are our vegetables and

fruits. Then, let the students create a plant out of food. Use carrot sticks for the roots, celery for the stem, lettuce for the leaves, and tomatoes for the fruit. Take a picture, and then eat it all up!

- Activity (Plant Growth Video) - Have the students watch the following video to see how plants grow:
  - https://www.youtube.com/watch?v=Xn-3PBM5-70

Listen While You Eat

Reading Assignment

- *DK Children's Encyclopedia* pg. 194 (Plants)

Book Suggestions

- *From Seed to Plant (Rookie Read-About Science)* by Allan Fowler
- *From Seed to Plant* by Gail Gibbons

Week 1 Notes

Week 2 Grid Schedule

Main Idea	
Flowers are the reproductive part of a plant.	
Supplies Needed	
Hands-on Projects	A tulip, Razor or knife, Magnifying glass, Q-tip
Coordinating Activities	Paint, Cake with flowers, A large White T-shirt (100% cotton), Cardboard, Flower, Masking Tape, Newspaper, Hammer

Weekly Schedule

	Day 1	Day 2	Day 3	Day 4
Lunch Items	❑ Make the flower science sandwich - read the meat, discuss the bread, and color the page.*	❑ Add some cheese to your sandwich with the hands-on project: Flower Dissection.*	❑ Read the *DK Children's Encyclopedia* pg. 103.	❑ Add some mayo to your sandwich with the coordinating activity: Field of Flowers.
Feast Fillers	❑ Choose one or more of the library books to read.	❑ Add some more flavor with the coordinating activity: Icing Flowers.	❑ Add some more spice with the coordinating activity: Nature Prints.	❑ Choose one or more of the library books to read.

** If you are short on time, these items will create a Bare-Bones Snack for your week.*

Week 2 List Schedule

Weekly Overview

Focus-of-the-Week

- Flowers are the reproductive part of a plant.

Supplies Needed

	Hands-on Project Materials
Hands-on Project Materials	A tulip, Razor or knife, Magnifying glass, Q-tip
Coordinating Activity Supplies	Paint, Cake with flowers, A large White T-shirt (100% cotton), Cardboard, Flower, Masking Tape, Newspaper, Hammer

Weekly Checklist

Bare-Bones Snack

- ❑ Make the flower science sandwich - read the meat, discuss the bread, and color the page.
- ❑ Add some cheese to your sandwich with the hands-on project: Flower Dissection.

Complete the Lunch

- ❑ Add some mayo to your sandwich with the coordinating activity: Field of Flowers.
- ❑ Read the *DK Children's Encyclopedia* pg. 103.

Making it a Feast

- ❑ Add some more spice with the coordinating activity: Nature Prints.
- ❑ Add some more flavor with the coordinating activity: Icing Flowers.
- ❑ Choose one or more of the library books to read.

Week 2: Flowers

The Science Sandwich

The Meat

Read the following introduction to the students (LM pg. 48, RN pg. 24):

I love flowers! Especially when they are a part of a bouquet given to me by the dreamy Cecil Sassafras.

My favorite flower, as you already know, is the crocus, which comes in purple, white, or yellow. It's not the best flower to pick and put on your table, but there is nothing like seeing the Alaskan tundra covered with crocus blooms!

Before we dig into learning about flowers, can you tell me what you already know about the blooming structure of a plant? (Pause to give time for the students to answer.)

Yes, that is so true! You are brilliant! Flowers come in all shapes, sizes, and colors. Most of them smell delicious, but some, like the corpse flower, smell like rotting flesh. All flowers give off a scent and have pretty-colored petals to attract pollinators, which is the main job of this part of the plant.

Flowers are the reproductive part of a plant. The blooms have all the right parts to produce a seed with a bit of help from an insect or from the wind.

All flowers begin as buds, which are tightly compacted. The bud blooms, or opens up, to reveal the parts of the flower. First there are petals, the brightly-colored blades that help to attract insects toward the center of the flower. In the center of the flower, we find the parts that work together to make a seed—the pistil, the anther, and the pollen. Pollinators move the pollen from the anthers, the shorter structures, to the pistil, the tall structure in the middle. We call this process pollination!

OK, your turn! Can you, with the help of your teacher, find the petals, pistil, and anther on the flower below?

The Bread

Discussion Questions

- ☐ Ask the students the following questions:
  - ? What is the job of a flower?
  - ? How do flowers attract pollinators?

Written Assignments

- ☐ Have the students color the coloring page found on LM pg. 49.
- ☐ Have the students add what they have learned to the flower notes mini-book on RN pg. 25. Then, have them glue the mini-book into their journal.

Cheesy Additions

Scientific Demonstration - Flower Dissection

In this demonstration project, you and the students will have a chance to observe all the parts of a flower. (Note—*The goal of this experiment is to have your students examine a flower. If they are not interested in hearing about all the parts, skip it and just let them cut open and examine the flower, while you answer any questions that they may have.*)

Materials Needed

- ✓ A tulip (or other single flower with clearly defined parts)
- ✓ Razor or knife
- ✓ Magnifying glass
- ✓ Q-tip

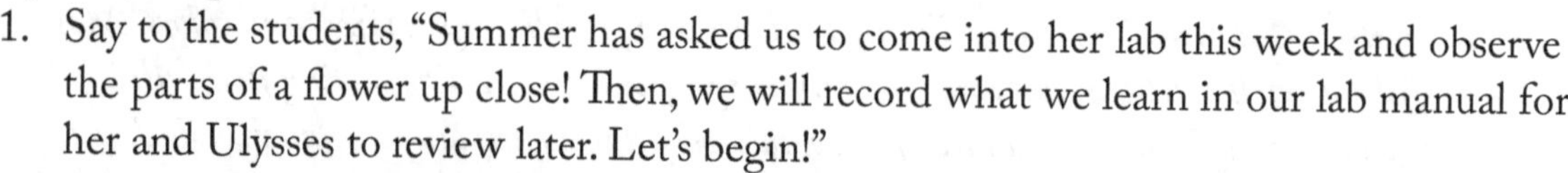

Steps to Complete

1. Say to the students, "Summer has asked us to come into her lab this week and observe the parts of a flower up close! Then, we will record what we learn in our lab manual for her and Ulysses to review later. Let's begin!"
2. Give each student a tulip bloom to examine. Use the diagram above to help point out the parts of the flower as they observe the bloom. Begin by pointing out the petals of the flower and explain that these are there to help attract insects to the flower.
3. Next, point out the anthers and the pollen on them. Share with the students that these are known as the male parts of a flower. Cut one of the anthers and use the magnifying glass to look at the pollen. (Note—*Be careful with the pollen, as it can stain clothing*).
4. Then, point out the pistil in the center and share that this is one of the female parts of a flower. Use a q-tip to show how a pollinator transfers the pollen to the top of the pistil. Cut out the pistol and split it in half so that your students can observe the inside.
5. Allow your students time to make additional observations before they fill out the demonstration sheet with the students found on LM pg. 50 or in their journal.

Results and Explanation

The students should see the different parts of the flower that Summer discussed in the introduction. (Note—*Don't forget to chart your plant's growth for this week!*)

The Mayo and More

Coordinating Activities

✂ Art (Field of Flowers) - Have the students paint their own field of flowers on the sheet found in the student workbook on LM pg. 51 or in their journal. Let your students' imaginations run free for this project; the results will be beautiful and interesting.

- Snack (Icing Flowers) - Give the students a piece of cake or a cupcake with some icing flowers to observe before they eat!
- Activity (Nature Prints) - Have the students use some of the flowers they have collected after a nature walk to make a print. You can find the directions for this project at the following website:
  - https://elementalscience.com/blogs/science-activities/nature-print-t-shirt

Listen while you eat

Reading Assignment

- *DK Children's Encyclopedia* pg. 103 (Flowers)

Book Suggestions

- *The Reason for a Flower* (Ruth Heller's World of Nature) by Ruth Heller
- *Planting a Rainbow* by Lois Ehler

WEEK 2 NOTES

Week 3 Grid Schedule

Main Idea	
Seeds contain tiny baby plants.	
Supplies Needed	
Hands-on Projects	3 Bean seeds, Paper towel, Plastic baggie, Tape, Water
Coordinating Activities	Red paint, Apples, Seeds and fruit with visible seeds, Glue, Paintbrush, Construction paper

Weekly Schedule

	Day 1	Day 2	Day 3	Day 4
Lunch Items	❑ Make the seeds science sandwich - read the meat, discuss the bread, and color the page.*	❑ Add some cheese to your sandwich with the hands-on project: Always Up.*	❑ Read the *DK Children's Encyclopedia* pg. 115.	❑ Add some mayo to your sandwich with the coordinating activity: Apple Prints.
Feast Fillers	❑ Choose one or more of the library books to read.	❑ Add some more flavor with the coordinating activity: Edible Seeds.	❑ Add some more spice with the coordinating activity: Seeds Collage.	❑ Choose one or more of the library books to read.

** If you are short on time, these items will create a Bare-Bones Snack for your week.*

Week 3 List Schedule

Weekly Overview

Focus-of-the-Week

- Seeds contain tiny baby plants.

Supplies Needed

	Hands-on Project Materials
Hands-on Project Materials	3 Bean seeds, Paper towel, Plastic baggie, Tape, Water
Coordinating Activity Supplies	Red paint, Apples, Seeds and fruit with visible seeds, Glue, Paintbrush, Construction paper

Weekly Checklist

Bare-Bones Snack

- ❑ Make the seeds sandwich - read the meat, discuss the bread, and color the page.
- ❑ Add some cheese to your sandwich with the hands-on project: Always Up.

Complete the Lunch

- ❑ Add some mayo to your sandwich with the coordinating activity: Apple Prints.
- ❑ Read the *DK Children's Encyclopedia* pg. 115.

Making it a Feast

- ❑ Add some more spice with the coordinating activity: Seeds Collage.
- ❑ Add some more flavor with the coordinating activity: Edible Seeds.
- ❑ Choose one or more of the library books to read.

Week 3: Seeds

The Science Sandwich

The Meat

Read the following introduction to the students (LM pg. 52, RN pg. 26):

Hot ham and cheese on multi-grain bread with whole grain mustard! It's one of the seed-packed sandwiches that inspired today's chat.

Multi-grain bread is packed with tiny seeds that are super good for your digestive tract—grains like quinoa, oats, and sunflower seeds. They make the bread super yummy.

But we are not here in the lab today to chat about bread! We are here to talk about seeds. Before I share some of what I know, can you tell me what you know about seeds? (Pause to give time for the students to answer.)

Once again, you do not disappoint! I am so happy to be able to share my lab with someone like you for this year!!

Let's get down to business! Last week, we talked about flowers and about how they contain all the parts needed to make a seed. This week, we are going to learn about that seed!!

Seeds contain a teeny, tiny baby plant that just needs the right amount of water and warmth to sprout and grow into a big mama (or dada) plant. Most of what is inside the seed is food. The baby plant needs all these food stores to have the energy to grow roots and leaves so that it can start making its own food.

But up at the top (or side – depending upon which way you are holding your seed), there's a little bulge. That little knobby is the very beginning of a plant, and we have a very special name for it. It's called a cotyledon, which basically means seed leaf.

And one day, that little seed leaf will grow into the roots and leaves of a big plant! OK, your turn! Can you, with the help of your teacher, find the part of the seed that will become the plant in the diagram?

The Bread

Discussion Questions

- ☐ Ask the students the following questions:
  - **?** What can you find inside of a seed?
  - **?** What will a seed do?

Written Assignment

- ☐ Have the students color the coloring page found on LM pg. 53.
- ☐ Have the students add what they have learned to the seed notes mini-book on RN pg. 27. Then, have them glue the mini-book into their journal.

Cheesy Additions

Scientific Demonstration - Always Up

In this demonstration project, you and the students will see that a seed always sends a stem and leaves up and roots down.

Materials Needed

- ✓ 3 Bean seeds
- ✓ Paper towel
- ✓ Plastic baggie
- ✓ Tape
- ✓ Water

Steps to Complete

1. Say to the students, "Today, Summer has asked us to test which way a plant grows from its seed. We'll watch our seeds sprout and then we will record our observations in our lab manual for her and Ulysses to review later. Let's get started!"
2. Dampen a paper towel, fold it, and place it in the bottom of the baggie.
3. Have the students place the three bean seeds at different angles on the paper towel.
4. Seal the baggie up and tape it to the side of your refrigerator.
5. Check the baggie each day for the next five days and record which way the seeds sprout on LM pg. 54 or in their journal.

Results and Explanation

The student should be able to observe that the seeds all send the stem and leaves up and the roots down, no matter in which position they begin. (Note—*Don't forget to chart your plant's growth for this week!*)

The Mayo and More

Coordinating Activities

- ✂ Art (Apple Prints) - Set out a plate with red paint on it for the students to use. Then, cut an apple in half horizontally instead of vertically. (*The seed pods will create a star pattern.*) Have the students dip one half of the apple in the paint and then use it to stamp a design on the sheet found on the activity page found on LM pg. 55 or in their journal.

- ✂ Snack (Eat Seeds) - Explain to the students that we can eat many different types of seeds and that we also eat fruits that contain seeds. Have several types of fruit/seeds that they can eat, such as cherry tomatoes, strawberries, blackberries, sunflower seeds, and pumpkin seeds. Enjoy trying the different fruits/seeds; talk about how they look and taste different.
- ✂ Activity (Seeds Collage) - Have the students paint a picture in glue on a piece of construction paper. Then use different types of seeds to create a collage out of their pictures.

Listen While You Eat

Reading Assignment

- *DK Children's Encyclopedia* pg. 115 (Fruit and seeds)

Book Suggestions

- *The Magic School Bus Plants Seeds: A Book About How Living Things Grow* by Joanna Cole
- *Seeds* by Ken Robbins
- *A Fruit Is a Suitcase for Seeds* by Jean Richards and Anca Hariton
- *Curious George Plants a Seed* (Curious George Early Readers) by H. A. Rey
- *A Seed Is Sleepy* by Dianna Hutts Aston and Sylvia Long

Week 3 Notes

Week 4 Grid Schedule

Main Idea	
Trees are large plants with woody stems called trunks.	
Supplies Needed	
Hands-on Projects	Crayons, Paper
Coordinating Activities	Pretzel Sticks, Green grapes, Paper Bags, Tissue Paper

Weekly Schedule

	Day 1	Day 2	Day 3	Day 4
Lunch Items	❑ Make the tree science sandwich - read the meat, discuss the bread, and color the page.*	❑ Add some cheese to your sandwich with the hands-on project: Backyard Bark.*	❑ Read the *DK Children's Encyclopedia* pg. 261.	❑ Add some mayo to your sandwich with the coordinating activity: Tree Sculpture.
Feast Fillers	❑ Choose one or more of the library books to read.	❑ Add some more flavor with the coordinating activity: Pretzel Tree.	❑ Add some more spice with the coordinating activity: Deciduous vs. Evergreen.	❑ Choose one or more of the library books to read.

** If you are short on time, these items will create a Bare-Bones Snack for your week.*

Week 4 List Schedule

Weekly Overview

Focus-of-the-Week

- Trees are large plants with woody stems called trunks.

Supplies Needed

	Hands-on Project Materials
Hands-on Project Materials	Crayons, Paper
Coordinating Activity Supplies	Pretzel Sticks, Green grapes, Paper Bags, Tissue Paper

Weekly Checklist

Bare-Bones Snack

- ❑ Make the tree science sandwich - read the meat, discuss the bread, and color the page.
- ❑ Add some cheese to your sandwich with the hands-on project: Backyard Bark.

Complete the Lunch

- ❑ Add some mayo to your sandwich with the coordinating activity: Tree Sculpture.
- ❑ Read the *DK Children's Encyclopedia* pg. 261.

Making it a Feast

- ❑ Add some more spice with the coordinating activity: Deciduous vs. Evergreen.
- ❑ Add some more flavor with the coordinating activity: Pretzel Tree.
- ❑ Choose one or more of the library books to read.

Week 4: Trees

The Science Sandwich

The Meat

Read the following introduction to the students (LM pg. 56, RN pg. 28):

I love a good cheese and apple sandwich with mustard on whole grain bread, but what really takes a sandwich like that over the top is to eat it under the very tree that the apple came from! I love leaning back on the trunk and looking up at the crown of the tree laden with apples. The cool breezes drifting around us lead to the best post-lunch naps.

But we are not here to talk about naps today. We are here to chat about trees! Can you tell me what you know about trees? (Pause to give time for the students to answer.)

Ahhhmazing! Trees can be either deciduous, meaning that they shed or lose their leaves in certain seasons, or evergreen, meaning that their leaves stay green year-round. The apple tree we sit under is a deciduous tree. The tree flowers in the spring and then the fruit develops and grows through the summer. In the fall, we harvest the apples just before the leaves turn colors and fall off.

But most of the trees around our lab are evergreen. These trees have needles that stick around all year long. And instead of the typical flowers and fruits, evergreen trees reproduce using cones.

Despite those differences, all trees have a few common parts. They all have a tough woody stem, called a trunk, that thickens as the tree grows older. From the trunk, the tree divides into branches, which form the crown of the tree. Under the ground, the tree has a huge root system that holds it in place.

OK, your turn! Can you, with the help of your teacher, find the parts of the tree – the trunk, the roots, and the crown – on the tree in the picture?

The Bread

Discussion Questions

- ☐ Ask the students the following questions:
  - **?** What are the two main types of trees?
  - **?** What are the three main parts of a tree?

Written Assignment

- ☐ Have the students color the coloring page found on LM pg. 57.

☐ Have the students add what they have learned to the tree notes mini-book on RN pg. 29. Then, have them glue the mini-book into their journal.

Cheesy Additions

Scientific Demonstration – Backyard Bark

In this demonstration project, you and the students will see the different patterns in bark.

Materials Needed

- ✓ Crayon
- ✓ Paper

Steps to Complete

1. Say to the students, "Remember when Summer shared about the trunk of a tree in our weekly science sandwich? Well, Summer also wanted you to know that the trunk is covered by a special protective layer called bark. And today, she has asked us to head outside, get a few samples of the designs of the bark in our area, and record our findings in our lab manual for her and Ulysses to review later. Let's get started!"
2. Head outside with the students to find several different kinds of trees to use for bark samples.
3. After you have selected a tree, have the students place a piece of paper on the tree trunk and rub on the top with a crayon until the shape of the bark appears. Then, use a field guide identify the different trees that the bark comes from. Label the page with the type of tree and any observations the students have about the bark.
4. Repeat this process until the students have three to five samples.
5. Once you are back inside, have them cut out sections of the bark rubbings they made and glue these onto LM pg. 58 or in their journal. Have them label each sample.

Results and Explanation

The students should see a variety of patterns in the bark from different trees. (Note—*Don't forget to chart your plant's growth for this week!*)

The Mayo and More

Coordinating Activities

✂ Art (Tree Sculpture) – Have the students make a sculpture of a tree using paper bags and tissue paper. The directions for this project can be found at the following website:

🖱 http://drawthelineat.blogspot.com/2012/02/fall-or-spring-trees.html

When they are done, take a picture and have the students glue it onto the activity page on LM pg. 59 or in their journal.

- ✂ Snack (Pretzel Tree) - Use pretzel sticks and green grapes to make a tree for snack. Cut all the grapes in half before giving the students a handful of pretzel sticks and grapes to make a tree. Have them use the pretzel sticks for the trunk, roots, and branches. Then, have them add lots of grapes for leaves before they eat their creations!
- ✂ Activity (Deciduous Vs. Evergreen) - Have the students use the information from the tree science sandwich and the encyclopedia reading to compare deciduous and evergreen trees. Have them tell you facts about each to write down on a piece of paper. You can show the similarities and differences with a Venn Diagram. A template for this can be found on pg. 229 of the Appendix.

Listen While You Eat

Reading Assignment

- *DK Children's Encyclopedia* pg. 261 (Trees)

Book Suggestions

- *A Tree Is a Plant (Let's-Read-and-Find... Science)* by Clyde Robert Bulla and Stacey Schuett
- *From Pinecone to Pine Tree (Scholastic News Nonfiction Readers: How Things Grow)* by Ellen Weiss

Week 4 Notes

UNIT 4: WEATHER

Unit 4 At-A-Glance

Unit Purpose

This unit is your student's first look at the world of earth science. In this unit, the students will learn the basics the weather found on our planet, Earth.

Weather Topics

- ✓ Week 1: The Sun
- ✓ Week 2: Clouds
- ✓ Week 3: Weather
- ✓ Week 4: Seasons

Supplies Needed

Week	Hands-on Project Materials	Coordinating Activity Supplies
1	Baking Dish (9 x 13 pan or similar), Foil, Clear plastic wrap, Graham crackers, Large marshmallows, Chocolate bar	White glue, Paintbrush, Several different colors of tissue paper (preferably yellow, orange and red)
2	Paper, Pencil	Light blue paint, Paintbrush, Glue, Cotton balls, 2 Eggs, Cream of tartar, Vanilla, Sugar
3	Clear glass jar, Jar lid or bowl, Ice cubes, Hot water	Eyedropper, Straw, Paper, Blue Jell-O, Cool Whip, String
4	Weather Stickers (Appendix pg. 231)	Magazine pictures, Bananas, Grapes, Strawberries, Raisins, Carrots, and Skewers, Paper, Colored Pencils

Week 1 Grid Schedule

Main Idea	
Heat from the sun makes life possible on the Earth.	
Supplies Needed	
Hands-on Projects	Baking Dish (9 x 13 pan or similar), Foil, Clear plastic wrap, Graham crackers, Large marshmallows, Chocolate bar
Coordinating Activities	White glue, Paintbrush, Several different colors of tissue paper (preferably yellow, orange and red)

Weekly Schedule

	Day 1	Day 2	Day 3	Day 4
Lunch Items	❑ Make the sun science sandwich - read the meat, discuss the bread, and color the page.*	❑ Add some cheese to your sandwich with the hands-on project: Solar Changes.*	❑ Read the *DK Children's Encyclopedia* pg. 247.	❑ Add some mayo to your sandwich with the coordinating activity: Tissue Paper Sun.
Feast Fillers	❑ Choose one or more of the library books to read.	❑ Add some more flavor with the coordinating activity: Solar S'mores.	❑ Add some more spice with the coordinating activity: Shadow Tag.	❑ Choose one or more of the library books to read.

** If you are short on time, this item will create a Bare-Bones Snack for your week.*

Week 1 List Schedule

Weekly Overview

Focus-of-the-Week

- Heat from the sun makes life possible on the Earth.

Supplies Needed

	Hands-on Project Materials
Hands-on Project Materials	Baking Dish (9 x 13 pan or similar), Foil, Clear plastic wrap, Graham crackers, Large marshmallows, Chocolate bar
Coordinating Activity Supplies	White glue, Paintbrush, Several different colors of tissue paper (preferably yellow, orange and red)

Weekly Checklist

Bare-Bones Snack

- ❑ Make the sun science sandwich - read the meat, discuss the bread, and color the page.
- ❑ Add some cheese to your sandwich with the hands-on project: Solar Changes.

Complete the Lunch

- ❑ Add some mayo to your sandwich with the coordinating activity: Tissue Paper Sun.
- ❑ Read the *DK Children's Encyclopedia* pg. 247.

Making it a Feast

- ❑ Add some more spice with the coordinating activity: Shadow Tag.
- ❑ Add some more flavor with the coordinating activity: Solar S'mores.
- ❑ Choose one or more of the library books to read.

Week 1: The Sun

The Science Sandwich

The Meat

Read the following introduction to the students (LM pg. 62, RN pg. 30):

Ulysses and I just got back from this amazing little sandwich shack, called the Solar Shack, where they serve all kinds of sunny treats. But my favorite by far is the sun-dried tomato grilled cheese on sourdough bread.

Lunch just doesn't get much better than that, especially when you consider how much work goes into a sandwich that sounds so simple.

But we are not here to discuss how to make sun-dried tomatoes! We are here to chat about the sun. Before we do that, can you tell me where the sun is? (Pause to give time for the students to answer.)

Yep! The sun appears up in our sky, but it's really way out at the center of our solar system. The sun has a very special job to do – it gives light and heat to the Earth. That's why it usually warmer during the day than it is at night when the sun is not shining on our part of the globe. This heat from the sun makes life as we know it possible on the Earth!

When an object, like a tree or a cloud, blocks out the rays of the sun, a shadow is created. And that shadow provides some much-needed shade on a hot day. In the shade, the light and heat from the sun's rays is diminished, so it feels a bit cooler on a sunny summer day.

Now it's your turn. Can you point out the sun in the picture? How about the shadow? On a hot sunny day, point to where you would want to set up your picnic.

The Bread

Discussion Questions

- [ ] Ask the students the following questions:
  - **?** What does the sun provide for us on Earth?
  - **?** What is created when the sun's rays are blocked?

Written Assignments

- [ ] Have the students color the coloring page found on LM pg. 63.
- [ ] Have the students add what they have learned to the sun notes mini-book on RN pg. 31. Then, have them glue the mini-book into their journal.

Cheesy Additions

Scientific Demonstration - Solar Changes

In this demonstration project, you and the students will observe how the sun's heat can change things.

Materials Needed

- ✓ Baking Dish (9 x 13 pan or similar)
- ✓ Foil
- ✓ Clear plastic wrap
- ✓ Graham crackers
- ✓ Large marshmallows
- ✓ Chocolate bar

Steps to Complete

1. Gather up the supplies needed to begin this project.
2. Say to the students, "Summer has asked us to observe how the sun's heat can change things. She and Ulysses have sent us the directions for using the sun's rays to create a warm, delicious snack! Then, we'll record our observations in our lab manual for her and Ulysses to review later. Let's begin!"
3. Have the students help you line the baking dish with foil. Then, have them set several graham crackers on the foil. Top the graham crackers with a piece of chocolate and then a marshmallow.
4. After that, tightly wrap plastic wrap over the top of the pan and set it outside in direct sunlight. Allow the s'mores to "cook" for thirty minutes before check on their progress. Once the marshmallow and chocolate are soft, your s'mores are ready to eat! (***Note** - The s'mores can take up to two hours to melt sufficiently depending on how hot the day is and how clear the day is.*)
5. Once they are done, have the students take a picture of the solar oven and fill out the demonstration sheet on LM pg. 64 or add their observations to their journal.

Results and Explanation

The students should see that the marshmallow and chocolate have softened and melted. This is because the rays from the sun contain energy in the form of light and heat. This energy from the sun makes life possible on Earth. It also helps to create weather on our planet by heating up air and water on the surface.

The Mayo and More

Coordinating Activities

✂ Art (Tissue Paper Sun) - Have the students make a sun collage with tissue paper. You will need white glue, a paintbrush, and several different colors of tissue paper (preferably yellow, orange, and red). Begin by thinning out the glue with a bit of water, so that it's easy for the students to paint with. Have your students use the thinned-out glue to paint the sun template on LM pg. 65 or in their journal. Then have the students put torn pieces of the tissue paper down on the glue to cover the Sun.

- Snack (Solar S'mores) - Eat the solar s'mores you made for the scientific demonstration.
- Activity (Shadow Tag) - Have the students play a game of shadow tag. See directions for this game here:
  - https://itsallkidsplay.ca/how-to-play-shadow-tag/

Listen While You Eat

Reading Assignment

- *DK Children's Encyclopedia* pg. 247 (Sun)

Book Suggestions

- *Hot and Bright: A Book about the Sun (Amazing Science: Exploring the Sky)* by Dana Meachen Rau and Denise Shea
- *A Sunny Day (First Step Nonfiction)* by Robin Nelson
- *The Sun: Our Nearest Star (Let's-Read-and-Find...)* by Franklyn M. Branley and Edward Miller
- *What Makes a Shadow? (Let's-Read-and-Find...)* by Clyde Robert Bulla and June Otani

Week 1 Notes

Week 2 Grid Schedule

Main Idea	
Clouds are made from water vapor in the sky.	
Supplies Needed	
Hands-on Projects	Paper, Pencil
Coordinating Activities	Light blue paint, Paintbrush, Glue, Cotton balls, 2 Eggs, Cream of tartar, Vanilla, Sugar

Weekly Schedule

	Day 1	Day 2	Day 3	Day 4
Lunch Items	❑ Make the cloud science sandwich - read the meat, discuss the bread, and color the page.*	❑ Add some cheese to your sandwich with the hands-on project: Cloudy Observations.*	❑ Read the *DK Children's Encyclopedia* pg. 64.	❑ Add some mayo to your sandwich with the coordinating activity: Fluffy Clouds.
Feast Fillers	❑ Choose one or more of the library books to read.	❑ Add some more flavor with the coordinating activity: Egg-White Clouds.	❑ Add some more spice with the coordinating activity: Cloud Matching.	❑ Choose one or more of the library books to read.

** If you are short on time, these items will create a Bare-Bones Snack for your week.*

Week 2 List Schedule

Weekly Overview

Focus-of-the-Week

- Clouds are made from water vapor in the sky.

Supplies Needed

	Hands-on Project Materials
Hands-on Project Materials	Paper, Pencil
Coordinating Activity Supplies	Light blue paint, Paintbrush, Glue, Cotton balls, 2 Eggs, Cream of tartar, Vanilla, Sugar

Weekly Checklist

Bare-Bones Snack

- ❑ Make the cloud science sandwich - read the meat, discuss the bread, and color the page.
- ❑ Add some cheese to your sandwich with the hands-on project: Cloudy Observations.

Complete the Lunch

- ❑ Add some mayo to your sandwich with the coordinating activity: Fluffy Clouds.
- ❑ Read the *DK Children's Encyclopedia* pg. 64.

Making it a Feast

- ❑ Add some more spice with the coordinating activity: Cloud Matching.
- ❑ Add some more flavor with the coordinating activity: Egg-White Clouds.
- ❑ Choose one or more of the library books to read.

Week 2: Clouds

The Science Sandwich

The Meat

Read the following introduction to the students (LM pg. 66, RN pg. 32):

There is nothing more relaxing than wrapping up a good picnic with a game of cloud shapes. You know – the game where you lie back and look up, guessing the shapes that the clouds are forming.

Ulysses always comes up with the most interesting ideas. But today, we are not talking about cloud shapes; we are going to chat about what makes clouds. Before I do that, can you tell me what you know about clouds? (Pause to give time for the students to answer.)

Brilliant! Clouds are made from tiny drops of water, called water vapor, in the sky. They form when warm air filled with these micro drops cools down.

The way a cloud looks depends upon how much water is in it and how fast it forms. If the cloud forms slowly, it will spread out in sheets. If the cloud forms quickly, it puff up into heaps, like marshmallows!

There are three main types of clouds, which are based on where you find them. Cirrus clouds are high and wispy. Alto clouds are mid-level clouds that can be puffy or flat. Stratus clouds form low, flat layers closest to the ground. There are also cumulus clouds, which are tall, puffy clouds that can grow and form between the layers.

Aren't clouds cool? Okie, dokie, now it's your turn – take a look at the clouds in the picture. How are they the same? How are they different?

The Bread

Discussion Questions

- ☐ Ask the students the following questions:
  - ? What are clouds made from?
  - ? Can you tell me about one of the types of clouds?

Written Assignments

- ☐ Have the students color the coloring page found on LM pg. 67.
- ☐ Have the students add what they have learned to the clouds notes mini-book on RN pg. 33. Then, have them glue the mini-book into their journal.

Cheesy Additions

Scientific Demonstration – Cloudy Observations

In this demonstration project, you and the students will have a chance to observe and draw clouds in the sky.

Materials Needed

- ✓ Paper
- ✓ Pencils

Steps to Complete

1. Say to the students, "Summer has asked us to head outside and observe the clouds we can see in the sky. Then, we will draw what we see in our lab manual for her and Ulysses to review later. Let's begin!"
2. Head outside to a spot where you can see the sky and allow the students to look up at the clouds.
3. Take as long as they remain interested and be sure to answer any questions they have. You can also try to identify the different types of clouds you see using the information from the introduction.
4. Have the students draw a few of the clouds they observed on the demonstration sheet found on LM pg. 68 or in their journal.

Results and Explanation

The students should see one or more of the different types of clouds that Summer discussed in the introduction.

The Mayo and More

Coordinating Activities

- ✂ Art (Fluffy Clouds) – Have the students create their own clouds on LM pg. 69 or in their journal. You will need light blue paint, a paintbrush, glue, and cotton balls. Have your student paint the page light blue all over. Once the paint dries have them stretch out the cotton balls into various shapes and glue those shapes onto the page as clouds.
- ✂ Snack (Egg-white Clouds) – Make a few edible clouds to eat for snack. Begin by beating two egg whites and ¼ tsp of cream of tartar until stiff peaks form. Next, add in ½ tsp vanilla and ¼ cup sugar and continue to beat until well incorporated. Drop spoonfuls on the mixture on a cookie sheet lined with foil and bake at 325°F for 10 min. Then, turn off the oven, but don't open the door. Let the egg-white clouds sit in the oven for 50 more minutes. Remove and eat. (*You can also dye some vanilla pudding light blue and float your clouds in the sky.*)

✂ ACTIVITY (CLOUD MATCHING) - Have the students match clouds by color and/or by size. Cut out the clouds on the Cloud Matching sheet found in the Appendix on pg. 230 to use for this activity.

LISTEN WHILE YOU EAT

READING ASSIGNMENT

- *DK Children's Encyclopedia* pg. 64 (Clouds)

BOOK SUGGESTIONS

- *Clouds (Let's-Read-and-Find... Science 1)* by Anne F. Rockwell and Frane Lessac
- *Little Cloud (Picture Puffins)* by Eric Carle
- *The Cloud Book* by Tomie dePaola

WEEK 2 NOTES

Week 3 Grid Schedule

Main Idea	
Weather is what is happening outside in the sky.	
Supplies Needed	
Hands-on Projects	Clear glass jar, Jar lid or bowl, Ice cubes, Hot water
Coordinating Activities	Eyedropper, Straw, Paper, Blue Jell-O, Cool Whip, String

Weekly Schedule

	Day 1	Day 2	Day 3	Day 4
Lunch Items	❑ Make the weather science sandwich - read the meat, discuss the bread, and color the page.*	❑ Add some cheese to your sandwich with the hands-on project: Weather in a Jar.*	❑ Read the *DK Children's Encyclopedia* pg. 271.	❑ Add some mayo to your sandwich with the coordinating activity: Weather Painting.
Feast Fillers	❑ Choose one or more of the library books to read.	❑ Add some more flavor with the coordinating activity: Jell-O Storms.	❑ Add some more spice with the coordinating activity: Weather Mobile.	❑ Choose one or more of the library books to read.

** If you are short on time, these items will create a Bare-Bones Snack for your week.*

Week 3 List Schedule

Weekly Overview

Focus-of-the-Week

- Weather is what is happening outside in the sky.

Supplies Needed

	Hands-on Project Materials
Hands-on Project Materials	Clear glass jar, Jar lid or bowl, Ice cubes, Hot water
Coordinating Activity Supplies	Eyedropper, Straw, Paper, Blue Jell-O, Cool Whip, String

Weekly Checklist

Bare-Bones Snack

- ❑ Make the weather sandwich - read the meat, discuss the bread, and color the page.
- ❑ Add some cheese to your sandwich with the hands-on project: Weather in a Jar.

Complete the Lunch

- ❑ Add some mayo to your sandwich with the coordinating activity: Weather Painting.
- ❑ Read the *DK Children's Encyclopedia* pg. 271.

Making it a Feast

- ❑ Add some more spice with the coordinating activity: Weather Mobile.
- ❑ Add some more flavor with the coordinating activity: Jell-O Storms.
- ❑ Choose one or more of the library books to read.

Week 3: Weather

The Science Sandwich

The Meat

Read the following introduction to the students (LM pg. 70, RN pg. 34):

Once, while visiting a friend's lab, Ulysses and I went to this restaurant called the Hurricane Grill and they had the best Blue Cheese Bacon Burger I have ever tasted on that side of the Mississippi!

Thankfully, while we were there, no hurricanes were forecasted, but we did have a few rainstorms, which brings me to our topic for today – weather! But before I share what I know, can you share what you know about weather? (Pause to give time for the students to answer.)

Cheers to your intellect! Weather is the word we use to describe what is happening in the atmosphere, or rather in the air and sky outside.

It can be foggy.

It can be sunny and hot.

It can be breezy or windy.

It can be cloudy and cool.

It can be raining. It can be snowing.

It can be . . . well, you get my point! There are lots of options when it comes to the weather.

There's a whole branch of science devoted to predicting the weather. And meteorologists work hard to share with us what the weather will be, but sometimes the weather just seems to have a mind of its own!

Okay, now it's your turn! Find a window and look outside, up at the sky. What is today's weather?

The Bread

Discussion Questions

- ☐ Ask the students the following questions:
  - ? What is weather?
  - ? What types of weather are there?

Written Assignment

- ☐ Have the students color the coloring page found on LM pg. 71.
- ☐ Have the students add what they have learned to the weather notes mini-book on RN pg. 35. Then, have them glue the mini-book into their journal.

Cheesy Additions

Scientific Demonstration – Weather in a Jar

In this demonstration project, you and the students will see a mini-rainstorm in a jar.

Materials Needed

- ✓ Clear glass jar
- ✓ Jar lid or bowl
- ✓ Ice cubes
- ✓ Hot water

Steps to Complete

1. Say to the students, "Today, Summer has asked us to observe how a rainstorm forms from the safety of our indoor lab. We'll watch what happens to the weather in our jar and then we will record our observations in our lab manual for her and Ulysses to review later. Let's get started!"
2. Fill the jar two-thirds of the way full with hot water. (***Note** – The jar will get very warm, so do not leave the students unsupervised at any point during this demonstration!!*)
3. Have the students quickly cover the jar with a bowl or an upside down jar lid. Have them fill the lid and bowl with ice cubes.
4. Observe the changes that take place over the next thirty minutes, adding observations to the demonstration sheet on LM pg. 72 or in their journal every 5 minutes.

Results and Explanation

The students should see condensation forming after a few minutes. If they wait long enough, they will begin to see droplets form and fall in the jar. The conditions created in the jar are very similar to the ones that produce storms and rain on Earth. The warm, moist air comes in contact with cool air. Then, the water vapor condenses, collects, and falls.

The Mayo and More

Coordinating Activities

✂ Art (Weather Painting) – Have the students create a masterpiece with "wind" and "rain." You will need an eyedropper, a straw, and a sheet of paper. Squeeze a bit of paint on the activity page found on LM pg. 73 or in their journal. Then, have the students use the straw to blow wind to move the paint around. Next, have the students use the eyedropper to rain down paint on the paper from varying heights.

- ✂ Snack (Jell-O Storms) - Make your favorite blue-colored Jell-O and fill a clear cup halfway with it for the rain. Then, top the rain Jell-O off with Cool Whip for clouds! (***Note** – You could use food coloring to tint the cool whip gray for more authentic rain clouds.*)
- ✂ Activity (Weather Mobile) - Have the students make a mobile showing the different types of weather. You will need string, two sticks, and a copy of the weather sticker templates found in the Appendix on pg. 231. (***Note** – You will use the weather sticker templates again next week.*) Begin by having the students choose two sticks from outside for a mobile. Have them color the weather mobile templates while you secure their two sticks together with string in a x-shape. Then punch holes in each of the weather pictures and one to each of the four ends of the sticks.

Listen while you eat

Reading Assignment

- *DK Children's Encyclopedia* pg. 271 (Weather)

Book Suggestions

- *Down Comes the Rain (Let's-Read-And-Find... Science: Stage 2)* by Franklyn Mansfield Branley and James Graham Hale
- *Oh Say Can You Say What's the Weather Today?: All About Weather (Cat in the Hat's Learning Library)* by Tish Rabe and Aristides Ruiz
- *What Will the Weather Be? (Let's-Read-and-Find... Science 2)* by Lynda Dewitt and Carolyn Croll

Week 3 Notes

Week 4 Grid Schedule

Main Idea	
Spring, summer, fall, and winter are all seasons.	
Supplies Needed	
Hands-on Projects	Weather Stickers (Appendix pg. 231)
Coordinating Activities	Magazine pictures, Bananas, Grapes, Strawberries, Raisins, Carrots, and Skewers, Paper, Colored Pencils

Weekly Schedule

	Day 1	Day 2	Day 3	Day 4
Lunch Items	❑ Make the seasons science sandwich - read the meat, discuss the bread, and color the page.*	❑ Add some cheese to your sandwich with the hands-on project: Weather Watch.*	❑ Read the *DK Children's Encyclopedia* pg. 221.	❑ Add some mayo to your sandwich with the coordinating activity: Seasons Collage.
Feast Fillers	❑ Choose one or more of the library books to read.	❑ Add some more flavor with the coordinating activity: Banana Snowmen.	❑ Add some more spice with the coordinating activity: Seasons Book.	❑ Choose one or more of the library books to read.

** If you are short on time, these items will create a Bare-Bones Snack for your week.*

Week 4 List Schedule

Weekly Overview

Focus-of-the-Week

- Spring, summer, fall, and winter are all seasons.

Supplies Needed

	Hands-on Project Materials
Hands-on Project Materials	Weather Stickers (Appendix pg. 231)
Coordinating Activity Supplies	Magazine pictures, Bananas, Grapes, Strawberries, Raisins, Carrots, and Skewers, Paper, Colored Pencils

Weekly Checklist

Bare-Bones Snack

- ❑ Make the seasons science sandwich - read the meat, discuss the bread, and color the page.
- ❑ Add some cheese to your sandwich with the hands-on project: Weather Watch.

Complete the Lunch

- ❑ Add some mayo to your sandwich with the coordinating activity: Seasons Collage.
- ❑ Read the *DK Children's Encyclopedia* pg. 221.

Making it a Feast

- ❑ Add some more spice with the coordinating activity: Seasons Book.
- ❑ Add some more flavor with the coordinating activity: Banana Snowmen.
- ❑ Choose one or more of the library books to read.

Week 4: Seasons

The Science Sandwich

The Meat

Read the following introduction to the students (LM pg. 74, RN pg. 36):

Here in our Alaskan Lab, we get to experience all four seasons, but three of those are much shorter than they are in the lower 48. Winter is long, which is the reason Ulysses and I eat lots of hot sandwiches, like the Hot Brown.

Warm chunks of turkey topped with bacon and drizzled with alfredo sauce. Slices of cool tomatoes and sandwiched between two toasted slices of country white – it's amazing! And certainly enough to keep you going on a cold winter day.

But we are not here to discuss the merits of a hot sandwich on a cold day – we are here to chat about the seasons. Before I continue, what do you know about the seasons? (Pause to give time for the students to answer.)

Wow! Those are some great tidbits! A season is a collection of days with a typical weather pattern. On earth, we have four seasons – spring, summer, fall, and winter. Sometimes people refer to fall as autumn, but that's a whole 'nother ball of wax!

Typically, winter has shorter days that can be filled with cold temperatures and snow. Around spring, it warms up and the flowers begin to bloom. During summer, the days are longer and hotter. And finally, fall comes along with a drop in the temperature and a change in the leaves, which leads us back into winter all over again!

Winter, spring, summer, and fall are all seasons, and each one typically sees a change in the weather. Okay, now it's your turn – can you guess what season it is now?

The Bread

Discussion Questions

- ☐ Ask the students the following questions:
  - **?** What are the four seasons?
  - **?** Can you tell me a bit about your favorite season?

Written Assignment

- ☐ Have the students color the coloring page found on LM pg. 75.
- ☐ Have the students add what they have learned to the seasons notes mini-book on RN pg. 37. Then, have them glue the mini-book into their journal.

Cheesy Additions

Scientific Demonstration - Weather Watch

In this demonstration project, you and the students will observe the weather over a week and record what they see.

Materials Needed

- ✓ Weather Stickers (Appendix pg. 231)

Steps to Complete

1. Say to the students, "Summer has asked that over the next week we observe and record the weather in our area. We'll add what we see using weather stickers in our lab manual for her and Ulysses to review later. Let's get started by looking outside to see today's weather!"
2. Have the students observe the weather each day for five days.
3. Each day, have them glue the appropriate weather watch stickers on the chart found on lab manual pg. 76 or in their journal.

Results and Explanation

The students should see a variety of weather over the week.

The Mayo and More

Coordinating Activities

- ✂ Art (Seasons Collage) - Have the students make a collage for the season you are in using pictures from magazines. For example, if you do this week during the winter, use pictures of snowflakes, bare trees, icicles, Christmas trees, and so on. Have the students glue the pictures on the activity page on LM pg. 77 or in their journal.
- ✂ Snack (Banana Snowmen) - Use bananas, grapes, strawberries, raisins, carrots, and skewers to make snowmen on a stick. You can see directions for this here:
  - http://onehandedcooks.com.au/recipe/christmas-banana-snowmen/
- ✂ Activity (Seasons Book) - Talk about the different things you see in each season. Then, have the students make a book with a page for each season. You can have them draw their own pictures or you can use stickers to complete the project. You can download a free template for this project here:
  - https://elementalscience.com/blogs/science-activities/seasons-hawk-talons

Listen while you eat

Reading Assignment

- *DK Children's Encyclopedia* pg. 221 (Seasons)

Book Suggestions

- *Watching the Seasons (Welcome Books)* by Edana Eckart
- *Sunshine Makes the Seasons (Let's-Read-and-Find... Science 2)* by Franklyn M. Branley and Michael Rex
- *Our Seasons* by Ranida T. Mckneally and Grace Lin

Week 4 Notes

Unit 5: Rocks

Unit 5 At-A-Glance

Unit Purpose

This unit is your student's first look at the world of geology. In this unit, the students will learn the basics of rocks and several common geological features.

Rock Topics

- ✓ Week 1: Rocks
- ✓ Week 2: Mountains
- ✓ Week 3: Volcanoes
- ✓ Week 4: Fossils

Supplies Needed

Week	Hands-on Project Materials	Coordinating Activity Supplies
1	Rocks, magnifying glass	Rocks collected for the demonstration, Paint, Butter, Graham cracker crumbs, Sweetened condensed milk, Chocolate chips, Peanut butter chips, Nuts
2	Globe or a topographical map	Colored paper, glue stick, Cheese, Air-dry clay, Paint
3	Toothpaste tube (full), Scissors, Empty yogurt container, Dirt	Paint, Hummus, Red pepper, White glue, Saline solution, Baking soda, White vinegar, Food coloring, Small bowl, Small cup
4	Air dry clay, Rubber insects or shells, Rolling pin	Paint, Several stamps or stencils with small plants or animals on them, Sugar cookie dough

Week 1 Grid Schedule

Main Idea				
Rocks come in different shapes and sizes, but they are all a mixture of minerals.				
Supplies Needed				
Hands-on Projects	Rocks, magnifying glass			
Coordinating Activities	Rocks collected for the demonstration, paint, Butter, Graham cracker crumbs, Sweetened condensed milk, Chocolate chips, Peanut butter chips, Nuts			
Weekly Schedule				
	Day 1	**Day 2**	**Day 3**	**Day 4**
Lunch Items	❑ Make the rock science sandwich - read the meat, discuss the bread, and color the page.*	❑ Add some cheese to your sandwich with the hands-on project: Rock Hunt.*	❑ Read the *DK Children's Encyclopedia* pg. 214.	❑ Add some mayo to your sandwich with the coordinating activity: Rock Stamping.
Feast Fillers	❑ Choose one or more of the library books to read.	❑ Add some more flavor with the coordinating activity: Sedimentary Rock Cookies.	❑ Add some more spice with the coordinating activity: Rock Band.	❑ Choose one or more of the library books to read.

** If you are short on time, this item will create a Bare-Bones Snack for your week.*

Week 1 List Schedule

Weekly Overview

Focus-of-the-Week

- Rocks come in different shapes and sizes, but they are all a mixture of minerals.

Supplies Needed

	Hands-on Project Materials
Hands-on Project Materials	Rocks, magnifying glass
Coordinating Activity Supplies	Rocks collected for the demonstration, paint, Butter, Graham cracker crumbs, Sweetened condensed milk, Chocolate chips, Peanut butter chips, Nuts

Weekly Checklist

Bare-Bones Snack

- ❑ Make the rock science sandwich - read the meat, discuss the bread, and color the page.
- ❑ Add some cheese to your sandwich with the hands-on project: Rock Hunt.

Complete the Lunch

- ❑ Add some mayo to your sandwich with the coordinating activity: Rock Stamping.
- ❑ Read the *DK Children's Encyclopedia* pg. 214.

Making it a Feast

- ❑ Add some more spice with the coordinating activity: Rock Band.
- ❑ Add some more flavor with the coordinating activity: Sedimentary Rock Cookies.
- ❑ Choose one or more of the library books to read.

Week 1: Rocks

The Science Sandwich

The Meat

Read the following introduction to the students (LM pg. 80, RN pg. 38):

When I was in school, my teacher taught us about layers in rock using a crunchy peanut butter and jelly sandwich that was mush until no human would want to eat it.

But you can relax, I shall not subject you to mushy sandwiches – unless it's a panini, because those are melty, delicious, crispy sandwich goodness. So, they don't really qualify as mushy sandwiches.

But there I go again – off on a sandwich tangent when we are supposed to be talking about rocks. Before we dig into that, can you tell me what you know about rocks? (Pause to give time for the students to answer.)

Well, you just rolled through sharing that!

Seriously, rocks are . . . well . . . rocky. These hard, natural objects can be found all over the Earth's surface. There are many different types of rocks, and they have many different uses. Rocks are used to build buildings, to form statues, and to create clay pots.

Rocks come in all shapes and sizes, but all rocks are a mixture of minerals. There are three main types of rocks. First, there are sedimentary rocks, which are formed as layers of crushed minerals and the decayed remains of plants or animals. Second, there are metamorphic rocks, which are rocks that have been changed by heat or pressure. And finally, there are igneous rocks, which start as melted rock that cools to form rocks!

Now it's your turn. Can you guess which rock in the picture below is a sedimentary rock? (The first rock is sandstone (sedimentary), the second is basalt (igneous), and the third is gneiss (metamorphic).)

The Bread

Discussion Questions

- ☐ Ask the students the following questions:
  - **?** What are rocks made of?
  - **?** What are the three types of rocks?

Written Assignments

- ☐ Have the students color the coloring page found on LM pg. 81.
- ☐ Have the students add what they have learned to rocks notes mini-book on RN pg. 39. Then, have them glue the mini-book into their journal.

Cheesy Additions

Scientific Demonstration - Rock Hunt

In this demonstration project, you and the students will find and observe rocks from your area.

Materials Needed

- ✓ Rocks
- ✓ Magnifying glass

Steps to Complete

1. Gather up the supplies needed to begin this project. (**Note** - *You may also want a bucket to carry the rocks that your students collects and a rock identification guide so that you can tell your students what types of rocks they have collected.*)
2. Say to the students, "Summer has asked us to find and observe the rocks that can be found in our area. We'll record our observations in our lab manual for her and Ulysses to add to their rock database. Let's begin!"
3. Take the students on a outdoors to hunt for rocks.
4. Allow them to collect whichever rocks they choose. If they would like to know what type of rock they picked up, tell them, but don't expect them to be able to classify rocks at this age.
5. Once you return home, have the students classify their rocks by shape, color, or size. Have them record how many rocks they found, (i.e., I found 6 white rocks, 2 gray ones, and 3 brown rocks) and take a picture of the rocks they collected. Have them add the photo and observations to the demonstration sheet on LM pg. 82 or to their journal.

Results and Explanation

The rocks you find will vary based on your location.

The Mayo and More

Coordinating Activities

- ✂ Art (Rock Stamping) - Have the students use the rocks they found during the rock hunt as stamps. You will need a variety of rocks and paint. Begin by having the students dip one of the rocks in the paint then using it to stamp the activity page on LM pg. 83 or in their journal. Repeat the process with the rest of the rocks.
- ✂ Snack (Sedimentary Rock Cookies) - Eat the sedimentary rock cookies with the students. You will need butter, graham crackers, condensed milk, chocolate chips, peanut butter chips, and nuts. Directions to make these cookies can be found here:
  - https://elementalscience.com/blogs/science-activities/summer-science-sedimentary-rock-cookies

✂ Activity (Rock Band) - Have the students use the rocks that were collected in the scientific demonstration to make a bit of music. You can have them tap different rocks together. You can have them tap the rocks on different surfaces. You can have them roll the rocks around a pie plate. Whatever you choose, have them students compare the sounds that the different rocks make.

Listen while you eat

Reading Assignment

- *DK Children's Encyclopedia* pg. 214 (Rocks and minerals)

Book Suggestions

- *Let's Go Rock Collecting (Let's-Read-And-Find... Science. Stage 2)* by Roma Gans and Holly Keller
- *Rocks: Hard, Soft, Smooth, and Rough (Amazing Science)* by Rosinsky, Natalie M, John and Matthew
- *If You Find a Rock* by Peggy Christian and Barbara Hirsch Lember

Week 1 Notes

Week 2 Grid Schedule

<table>
<tr><th colspan="5">Main Idea</th></tr>
<tr><td colspan="5">Mountains are tall, rocky bumps on the surface of the Earth.</td></tr>
<tr><th colspan="5">Supplies Needed</th></tr>
<tr><td>Hands-on Projects</td><td colspan="4">Globe or a topographical map</td></tr>
<tr><td>Coordinating Activities</td><td colspan="4">Colored paper, glue stick, Cheese, Air-dry clay, Paint</td></tr>
<tr><th colspan="5">Weekly Schedule</th></tr>
<tr><th></th><th>Day 1</th><th>Day 2</th><th>Day 3</th><th>Day 4</th></tr>
<tr><td>Lunch Items</td><td>❑ Make the mountain science sandwich - read the meat, discuss the bread, and color the page.*</td><td>❑ Add some cheese to your sandwich with the hands-on project: Mountain Ranges.*</td><td>❑ Read the DK Children's Encyclopedia pg. 172.</td><td>❑ Add some mayo to your sandwich with the coordinating activity: Torn Paper Mountains.</td></tr>
<tr><td>Feast Fillers</td><td>❑ Choose one or more of the library books to read.</td><td>❑ Add some more flavor with the coordinating activity: Cheese Ranges.</td><td>❑ Add some more spice with the coordinating activity: Clay Mountain.</td><td>❑ Choose one or more of the library books to read.</td></tr>
</table>

** If you are short on time, these items will create a Bare-Bones Snack for your week.*

Week 2 List Schedule

Weekly Overview

Focus-of-the-Week

- Mountains are tall, rocky bumps on the surface of the Earth.

Supplies Needed

	Hands-on Project Materials
Hands-on Project Materials	Globe or a topographical map
Coordinating Activity Supplies	Colored paper, glue stick, Cheese, Air-dry clay, Paint

Weekly Checklist

Bare-Bones Snack

- ❑ Make the mountain science sandwich - read the meat, discuss the bread, and color the page.
- ❑ Add some cheese to your sandwich with the hands-on project: Mountain Ranges.

Complete the Lunch

- ❑ Add some mayo to your sandwich with the coordinating activity: Torn Paper Mountains.
- ❑ Read the *DK Children's Encyclopedia* pg. 172.

Making it a Feast

- ❑ Add some more spice with the coordinating activity: Clay Mountain
- ❑ Add some more flavor with the coordinating activity: Cheese Ranges.
- ❑ Choose one or more of the library books to read.

Week 2: Mountains

The Science Sandwich

The Meat

Read the following introduction to the students (LM pg. 84, RN pg. 40):

I love a picnic lunch! Ulysses and I have this special spot we go to when we need to get out of the office for a sandwich-filled excursion. It's on a rocky outcrop and has an amazing view of the mountains.

We'd love for you to visit and share a sandwich or two with us there. You can bring your favorite lunch and we can swap science stories, but until then, how about you tell me what you already know about mountains? (Pause to give time for the students to answer.)

That was very interesting!

Mountains are tall rocky bumps – or rather features – on the surface of the Earth. They can have steep sides called slopes. And the very tippy top of the mountain is called the summit. Some mountains are so tall that they have a point, called the tree line, where the trees no longer grow.

Mountains are found on every continent on the globe. And every large land mass on the Earth has a row of mountains called a range. Here in North America, where our lab is located, we have two major ranges – the Appalachians and the Rockies.

Now it's your turn. Can you point out the slopes, tree line, and summit on the mountains below?

The Bread

Discussion Questions

- ☐ Ask the students the following questions:
  - **?** What are mountains?
  - **?** What is a row of mountains called?

Written Assignments

- ☐ Have the students color the coloring page found on LM pg. 85.
- ☐ Have the students add what they have learned to the mountains notes mini-book on RN pg. 41. Then, have them glue the mini-book into their journal.

Cheesy Additions

Scientific Demonstration - Mountain Ranges

In this demonstration project, you and the students will find and identify the different mountain ranges around the globe.

Materials Needed

✓ Globe or a topographical map

Steps to Complete

1. Say to the students, "Summer has asked us to learn a bit more about the different mountain ranges found on Earth. We are going to use a globe (or a topographical map) to find and identify the major mountain ranges around the globe. These mountains appear as raised bumps on the globe (or darker regions, more contoured regions on the map). Once we find the mountain ranges on the list, we'll use different colors to show where they are on the map in our lab manual for Summer and Ulysses to review later. Let's begin!"
2. Pull out the globe (or map) and help the students look for the following mountain ranges:
   - ? North America - Rocky Mountains, Appalachian Mountains
   - ? South America - Andes Mountains
   - ? Europe - The Alps
   - ? Africa - Atlas Mountains
   - ? Asia - Himalayan Mountains
   - ? Australia - The Great Dividing Range
3. Have the students color the area where the mountain range is and add that color to the key on the map found on the demonstration sheet found on LM pg. 86 or on a map you draw in their journal.

Results and Explanation

The point of this activity is to give the students some time to practice looking at and understanding the different parts of maps.

The Mayo and More

Coordinating Activities

✂ Art (Torn Paper Mountains) - Have the students make a picture of layered mountains using torn paper on the activity sheet on LM pg. 87. You will need colored paper and a glue stick for this project. Directions for making torn paper mountains can be found here:

🖱 http://www.3dinosaurs.com/wordpress/index.php/torn-paper-mountains/

- ✂ Snack (Cheese Ranges) - Cut several slices of cheese and then shape those into tall mountain-like triangles. Lay them out on a plate in a line to make a cheesy mountain range snack!
- ✂ Activity (Clay Mountain) - Have the students make a model of a mountain using air-dry clay and paint. You can use the mountain pictured on the assigned encyclopedia pages or create your own.

Listen While You Eat

Reading Assignment

- *DK Children's Encyclopedia* pg. 172 (Mountains)

Book Suggestions

- *Mountains* by Seymour Simon
- *How Mountains Are Made (Let's-Read-and-Find... Science 2)* by Kathleen Weidner Zoehfeld and James Graham Hale

Week 2 Notes

Week 3 Grid Schedule

Main Idea	
Volcanoes explode hot, sticky rock from inside the Earth.	
Supplies Needed	
Hands-on Projects	Toothpaste tube (full), Scissors, Empty yogurt container, Dirt
Coordinating Activities	Paint, Hummus, Red pepper, White glue, Saline solution, Baking soda, White vinegar, Food coloring, Small bowl, Small cup

Weekly Schedule				
	Day 1	**Day 2**	**Day 3**	**Day 4**
Lunch Items	❑ Make the volcano science sandwich - read the meat, discuss the bread, and color the page.*	❑ Add some cheese to your sandwich with the hands-on project: Toothpaste Volcano.*	❑ Read the *DK Children's Encyclopedia* pg. 268.	❑ Add some mayo to your sandwich with the coordinating activity: Volcanic Art.
Feast Fillers	❑ Choose one or more of the library books to read.	❑ Add some more flavor with the coordinating activity: Hummus Volcano.	❑ Add some more spice with the coordinating activity: Volcano Slime.	❑ Choose one or more of the library books to read.

** If you are short on time, these items will create a Bare-Bones Snack for your week.*

Week 3 List Schedule

Weekly Overview

Focus-of-the-Week

- Volcanoes explode hot, sticky rock from inside the Earth.

Supplies Needed

	Hands-on Project Materials
Hands-on Project Materials	Toothpaste tube (full), Scissors, Empty yogurt container, Dirt
Coordinating Activity Supplies	Paint, Hummus, Red pepper, White glue, Saline solution, Baking soda, White vinegar, Food coloring, Small bowl, Small cup

Weekly Checklist

Bare-Bones Snack

- ❑ Make the volcano sandwich - read the meat, discuss the bread, and color the page.
- ❑ Add some cheese to your sandwich with the hands-on project: Toothpaste Volcano.

Complete the Lunch

- ❑ Add some mayo to your sandwich with the coordinating activity: Volcanic Art.
- ❑ Read the *DK Children's Encyclopedia* pg. 268.

Making it a Feast

- ❑ Add some more spice with the coordinating activity: Volcano Slime.
- ❑ Add some more flavor with the coordinating activity: Hummus Volcano.
- ❑ Choose one or more of the library books to read.

Week 3: Volcanoes

The Science Sandwich

The Meat

Read the following introduction to the students (LM pg. 88, RN pg. 42):

I love a good grilled cheese sandwich – the bread is crunchy, and the cheese is all melty. Yum!

But you know how the cheese sometimes oozes out of the place you just took a bite? That oozing always makes me think about volcanoes!

Why, you ask? Well, I'll tell you in just a moment. Before that, can you tell me what you know about volcanoes? (Pause to give time for the students to answer.)

Wow – that is fascinating! Back to the cheese – the molten cheese to be more precise. The oozing cheese is melted, just like the rock that oozes or explodes out of a volcano. Thank goodness the cheese doesn't explode out of our sandwiches!!

Anywhoo, under what we can see of a volcano is a whole bunch of hot rock, called magma. This molten, or melted, rock comes from deep inside the Earth. When the magma gets too hot, pressure builds up, and eventually . . . BOOM!

The volcano blows its top or sometimes the magma just oozes out depending on how much pressure there is. But when this eruption happens, ash and hot, sticky rock spill out. And now that the magma that was inside the Earth is outside, we call it lava. And when the lava cools, it forms igneous rocks. How cool is that!

Volcanoes are found all over the world, including under the sea. And they come in all shapes and sizes, but the most recognizable shape in the cinder cone volcano, which you can see in the picture.

The Bread

Discussion Questions

- ☐ Ask the students the following questions:
  - **?** What is a volcano?
  - **?** What is magma called once it comes out of the volcano?

Written Assignment

- ☐ Have the students color the coloring page found on LM pg. 89.
- ☐ Have the students add what they have learned to the volcano notes mini-book on RN pg. 43. Then, have them glue the mini-book into their journal.

Cheesy Additions

Scientific Demonstration - Toothpaste Volcano

In this demonstration project, you and the students will see a small scale version of how a volcano erupts.

Materials Needed

- ✓ Toothpaste tube (full)
- ✓ Scissors
- ✓ Empty yogurt container
- ✓ Dirt

Steps to Complete

1. Say to the students, "Today, Summer has asked us to observe a toothpaste volcano eruption! We'll watch what happens and observe how the toothpaste erupts out of the dirt, and then we will record our observations in our lab manual for her and Ulysses to review later. Let's get started!"
2. (***Adults Only***) Use a pair of scissors or a knife to cut a hole large enough to fit the tip of a toothpaste tube on the bottom of an empty plastic yogurt container.
3. Have the students remove the cap from a toothpaste tube, and then insert the open tube into the hole.
4. Gently fill the yogurt container about two-thirds of the way full with dirt and pack it down just a bit.
5. Then, have the students squeeze the toothpaste tube as you hold the container and observe what happens!
6. Once the eruption is over, have them add their observations to the demonstration sheet on LM pg. 90 or in their journal.

Results and Explanation

The students should see that after a bit of squeezing, the toothpaste pushes its way out, or erupts, from the dirt.

The Mayo and More

Coordinating Activities

- ✂ Art (Volcanic Art) - Give the students some black, gray, orange, and red paint. Have them paint their own volcano on LM pg. 91 or in their journal. You can also add some texture to their volcano by adding salt or cornstarch to the paint.
- ✂ Snack (Hummus Volcano) - Make a volcano-shaped snack using hummus and red pepper strips. Start by spreading some hummus on one half of a plate in the shape of a triangle

volcano. Then, lay out the strips of red pepper to look like lava exploding out of the top of your hummus volcano!

- Activity (Volcano Slime) - Make a batch of bubbling, fizzing slime with your students. You will need white glue, saline solution, baking soda, white vinegar, food coloring, small bowl, and small cup. Get directions on how to make volcano slime here:
  - https://littlebinsforlittlehands.com/fizzing-slime-volcano/

Listen While You Eat

Reading Assignment

- *DK Children's Encyclopedia* pg. 268 (Volcanoes)

Book Suggestions

- *National Geographic Readers: Volcanoes!* by Anne Schreiber
- *Jump into Science: Volcano!* by Ellen J. Prager and Nancy Woodman
- *Volcanoes (Let's-Read-and-Find... Science 2)* by Franklyn M. Branley and Megan Lloyd
- *The Magic School Bus Blows Its Top: A Book About Volcanoes (Magic School Bus)* by Gail Herman and Bob Ostrom

Week 3 Notes

Week 4 Grid Schedule

Main Idea	
Fossils are imprints of long-gone plants or animals.	

Supplies Needed	
Hands-on Projects	Air dry clay, Rubber insects or shells, Rolling pin
Coordinating Activities	Paint, Several stamps or stencils with small plants or animals on them, Sugar cookie dough

Weekly Schedule

	Day 1	Day 2	Day 3	Day 4
Lunch Items	❑ Make the fossil science sandwich - read the meat, discuss the bread, and color the page.*	❑ Add some cheese to your sandwich with the hands-on project: Impression Fossils.*	❑ Read the *DK Children's Encyclopedia* pg. 111.	❑ Add some mayo to your sandwich with the coordinating activity: Fossilized Art.
Feast Fillers	❑ Choose one or more of the library books to read.	❑ Add some more flavor with the coordinating activity: Cookie Fossils.	❑ Add some more spice with the coordinating activity: Fossil Hunt.	❑ Choose one or more of the library books to read.

** If you are short on time, these items will create a Bare-Bones Snack for your week.*

Week 4 List Schedule

Weekly Overview

Focus-of-the-Week

- Fossils are imprints of long-gone plants or animals.

Supplies Needed

	Hands-on Project Materials
Hands-on Project Materials	Air dry clay, Rubber insects or shells, Rolling pin
Coordinating Activity Supplies	Paint, Several stamps or stencils with small plants or animals on them, Sugar cookie dough

Weekly Checklist

Bare-Bones Snack

- ❑ Make the fossil science sandwich - read the meat, discuss the bread, and color the page.
- ❑ Add some cheese to your sandwich with the hands-on project: Impression Fossils.

Complete the Lunch

- ❑ Add some mayo to your sandwich with the coordinating activity: Fossilized Art.
- ❑ Read the *DK Children's Encyclopedia* pg. 111.

Making it a Feast

- ❑ Add some more spice with the coordinating activity: Fossil Hunt.
- ❑ Add some more flavor with the coordinating activity: Cookie Fossils.
- ❑ Choose one or more of the library books to read.

Week 4: Fossils

The Science Sandwich

The Meat

Read the following introduction to the students (LM pg. 92, RN pg. 44):

So, do you remember that teacher I told you about at the beginning of our chat about rocks? The only who mushed the humble PB&J sandwich for science?

Well, she also thought it was a good idea to smash gummy bears in bread to teach us about fossils – she obviously did not love a good sandwich as much as Ulysses and I do.

I still shudder at the memory of that glistening gummy impression in some of the finest sourdough bread our little town offered.

But I digress. We are not here to chat about my old school memories; we are here to learn about fossils and before we do that, can you tell me what you know about fossils? (Pause to give time for the students to answer.)

You never fail to impress!! We find fossils in rocks all over the Earth. They are the remains of plants or animals that died many years ago.

When these living things died, they got stuck in the mud, and as time went by, more mud pressed on top of them. Eventually, there was so much weight that the mud turned into rock.

Over time, the living thing disappeared or decayed. All that was left was the imprint, or impression, of that plant or animal, on the rock.

Now it's your turn. Can you guess what made the imprints on the fossils in the picture?

The Bread

Discussion Questions

- ☐ Ask the students the following questions:
  - **?** What is a fossil?
  - **?** How are fossils formed?

Written Assignment

- ☐ Have the students color the coloring page found on LM pg. 93.
- ☐ Have the students add what they have learned to the fossil notes mini-book on RN pg. 45. Then, have them glue the mini-book into their journal.

Cheesy Additions

Scientific Demonstration - Impression Fossils

In this demonstration project, you and the students will see a shortened version of how impression fossils are made.

Materials Needed

- ✓ Air dry clay
- ✓ Rubber insects or shells
- ✓ Rolling pin

Steps to Complete

1. Say to the students, "Summer has asked that we learn how impression fossils are made. She sent over some directions for us to follow to make our own. Then, we'll take a picture of what we create and put it in our lab manual for her and Ulysses to review later. Let's get started!"
2. Have the students roll out the clay into a flat disc.
3. Then, have them place the rubber insects or shells in various places in the clay. Have them gently press the objects into the clay before picking them up.
4. The students should see that the objects left a print, or impression, behind. Have them take a picture or draw the fossil they created on the demonstration sheet found on LM pg. 94 or in their journal. (***Note** - You can set aside the clay model to let it dry overnight and have the students paint it the next day.*)

Results and Explanation

The students should see that the rubber insects or shells left an impression in their clay rock. This process is a shortened look at how impression fossils are made.

The Mayo and More

Coordinating Activities

- ✂ Art (Fossilized Art) - Have the students make a fossilized rock painting. You will need paint and several stamps or stencils, i.e., ones with a leaf, starfish, or other small plant or animal on them. Begin by having the students use gray or brown paint to paint a rock on LM pg. 95 or in their journal. Then, have the students use another color of paint and the stamps or stencils with to create "fossils" on their rocks.
- ✂ Snack (Cookie Fossils) - Make your favorite sugar cookie dough recipe. Have you students make rocks out of the cookies and then using forks, spoon, knives, or fingers, create fossils on the cookies.
- ✂ Activity (Fossil Hunt) - Take the students outside to look for fossils in nature. Although

there are places that are easier to find fossils, these impressions of the past can be found anywhere. If fossils are not easy to find in your area, you might want to have a piece on hand to observe.

Listen While You Eat

Reading Assignment

- *DK Children's Encyclopedia* pg. 111 (Fossils)

Book Suggestions

- *Mary Anning: Fossil Hunter* by Sally M. Walker and Phyllis V. Saroff
- *Viewfinder: Fossils* by Douglas Palmer and Neil D. L. Clark
- *What Do You Know About Fossils? (20 Questions: Science)* by Suzanne Slade
- *Fossils Tell of Long Ago (Let's-Read-and-Find Out Science 2)* by Aliki

Week 4 Notes

UNIT 6: SPACE

Unit 6 At-A-Glance

Unit Purpose

This unit is your student's first look at the world of astronomy. In this unit, the students will learn the basics of the things we see in the night sky and our solar system.

Space Topics

- ✓ Week 1: The Moon
- ✓ Week 2: Astronauts
- ✓ Week 3: Our Solar System
- ✓ Week 4: Constellations

Supplies Needed

Week	Hands-on Project Materials	Coordinating Activity Supplies
1	8 Sandwich-style cookies, Picture of the phases of the moon	Small balloon, Newspaper, Flour, Water, Salt, Paint, Picture of the moon, Bananas, Toothpicks, Melting chocolate
2	3 Balloons, Thick fabric (such as a woolen or fleece scarf), Thin fabric (such as a thin cotton T-shirt or pillowcase), Warm water	Markers, Picture of the student's face, Freeze-dried (or dehydrated) food, Toilet paper
3	Labeled picture of our solar system (Appendix pg. 233), Blank solar system template (Appendix pg. 234), Pencil	Black crayon or chalk pastel, Picture of the Milky Way galaxy, Silver glitter, Glue, Different types of fruit, Elastic string, Different kinds of beads
4	Foil, Toilet Paper Tube, Pin, Small flashlight, Constellation pictures (Appendix pg. 235), Rubber band, Sharpie marker	Gold star stickers, White crayon, Paper, Dark blue paint, Plain cupcakes, Blue and yellow frosting

Week 1 Grid Schedule

<table>
<tr><th colspan="5">Main Idea</th></tr>
<tr><td colspan="5">The moon orbits the Earth and can be seen in the night sky.</td></tr>
<tr><th colspan="5">Supplies Needed</th></tr>
<tr><td>Hands-on Projects</td><td colspan="4">8 Sandwich-style cookies, Picture of the phases of the moon</td></tr>
<tr><td>Coordinating Activities</td><td colspan="4">Small balloon, Newspaper, Flour, Water, Salt, Paint, Picture of the moon, Bananas, Toothpicks, Melting chocolate</td></tr>
<tr><th colspan="5">Weekly Schedule</th></tr>
<tr><td></td><td>Day 1</td><td>Day 2</td><td>Day 3</td><td>Day 4</td></tr>
<tr><td>Lunch Items</td><td>❑ Make the moon science sandwich - read the meat, discuss the bread, and color the page.*</td><td>❑ Add some cheese to your sandwich with the hands-on project: Moon Cookies.*</td><td>❑ Read the DK Children's Encyclopedia pg. 171.</td><td>❑ Add some mayo to your sandwich with the coordinating activity: Moon Model.</td></tr>
<tr><td>Feast Fillers</td><td>❑ Choose one or more of the library books to read.</td><td>❑ Add some more flavor with the coordinating activity: Banana Moons.</td><td>❑ Add some more spice with the coordinating activity: Phases Booklet.</td><td>❑ Choose one or more of the library books to read.</td></tr>
</table>

** If you are short on time, this item will create a Bare-Bones Snack for your week.*

Week 1 List Schedule

Weekly Overview

Focus-of-the-Week

- The moon orbits the Earth and can be seen in the night sky.

Supplies Needed

	Hands-on Project Materials
Hands-on Project Materials	8 Sandwich-style cookies, Picture of the phases of the moon
Coordinating Activity Supplies	Small balloon, Newspaper, Flour, Water, Salt, Paint, Picture of the moon, Bananas, Toothpicks, Melting chocolate

Weekly Checklist

Bare-Bones Snack

- ❑ Make the moon science sandwich - read the meat, discuss the bread, and color the page.
- ❑ Add some cheese to your sandwich with the hands-on project: Moon Cookies.

Complete the Lunch

- ❑ Add some mayo to your sandwich with the coordinating activity: Moon Model.
- ❑ Read the *DK Children's Encyclopedia* pg. 171.

Making it a Feast

- ❑ Add some more spice with the coordinating activity: Banana Moons.
- ❑ Add some more flavor with the coordinating activity: Phases Booklet.
- ❑ Choose one or more of the library books to read.

Week 1: The Moon

The Science Sandwich

The Meat

Read the following introduction to the students (LM pg. 98, RN pg. 46):

Cheese. Any good sandwich maker knows that a good cheese can make all the difference.

And so maybe it was some crazy deli-owner who started the rumor that the moon was made of cheese. Maybe that was part of his plan to get people to try his sandwiches.

I don't know, but Ulysses and I do know that the moon is not made of cheese. It's made of... wait, before I share that – what do you know about the moon? (Pause to give time for the students to answer.)

Wow, that's interesting info! Did you know that the moon is our closest space-neighbor? It goes around, or orbits, the Earth in the same way that the Earth orbits the Sun. It takes about 27 days to go around the Earth.

As the moon moves, parts of it are "lit" by the sun, which makes the moon look like it is a shining beacon in the night sky. The moon also appears to be changing shape night after night. We call these different shapes phases, and the pattern they follow the lunar cycle.

It all starts with a full moon. Then, the moon appears as if it is disappearing or waning until it gets all swallowed up in darkness. This is called the new moon and after that happens, the moon starts appearing, or waxing, until it gets to a full moon and the cycle starts all over again!

Now it's your turn. Can you point out below the full moon and the new moon? Can you show where the moon is waning (disappearing) and where it is waxing (appearing)?

The Bread

Discussion Questions

- ☐ Ask the students the following questions:
  - **?** Where does the moon travel?
  - **?** How does the moon shine?
  - **?** What do you remember about the lunar cycle?

Written Assignments

- ☐ Have the students color the coloring page found on LM pg. 99.
- ☐ Have the students add what they have learned to moon notes mini-book on RN pg. 47. Then, have them glue the mini-book into their journal.

Cheesy Additions

Scientific Demonstration - Moon Cookies

In this demonstration project, you and the students will observe and create a representation of the phases of the moon.

Materials Needed

- ✓ 8 Sandwich-style cookies
- ✓ Picture of the phases of the moon (template on Appendix pg. 232)

Steps to Complete

1. Gather up the supplies needed to begin this project.
2. Say to the students, "Summer has asked us to show more about the phases of the moon with cookies! She wrote the following for us to read beforehand:

   Hi-ya peeps - for this demo, Ulysses and I felt you needed a bit more info. Remember back in our meat sandwich, we shared about how the moon went through phases? Well, here's a bit more about the phases - a full moon is when it appears as if the entire moon is lit. After this, the moon begins disappearing or waning. The next phase is the gibbous moon, when it appears as if about three-quarters of the moon is lit. Next is the last quarter, when it appears as if half the moon is lit. Then, we have the crescent moon, phase when it appears as if only a quarter of the moon is lit. And finally, the moon disappears, which is referred to as a new moon. After that, the moon goes through the phases once more, but in reverse. This time, the moon is appearing or waxing.

   Now that we know a bit more about the phases, we are going to create them with cookies and then depict our findings in our lab manual for her and Ulysses to add to their rock database. Let's begin!"
3. Have the students begin by opening one of the sandwich-style cookies. Have them use the half with icing for the full moon and the half without icing for the new moon.
4. Have the students continue to open up the cookies and remove a portion of the icing to match the different phases of the moon, using the picture you provided them as a guide.
5. When they are done creating the moon cookies, have the students color the portions of the moons under each phase on the demonstration sheet on LM pg. 100 or to their journal.

Results and Explanation

The students should see the basic phases of the moon. Be sure to go back and review the phases after the students have finished creating their moon cookies.

The Mayo and More

Coordinating Activities

- Art (Moon Model) - Have the students make a paper mache model of the moon. You will need the following supplies: small balloon, newspaper, 1 cup of flour, ½ cup of water, 2 tablespoons of salt, paint, and a picture of the moon. Have the students blow up the balloon. Next, have them tear the newspaper into strips. As they are working on the newspaper strips, use the flour, water, and salt to make a thick paste. You can add more or less water to gain the desired consistency. Then, have the students dip the strips into the paste mixture and cover the balloon with one layer. Wait 30 minutes before having them add a second and third layer if necessary. Finally, set the paper mache moon in a place to dry. Once it is dry, have the students use the moon picture to paint it like the moon. Take a picture and add it to the activity sheet on LM pg. 101.
- Snack (Banana Moons) - To make banana moons, you will need bananas, toothpicks, and melting chocolate. Slice bananas into round moon shapes and melt the chocolate according to the package directions. Then using toothpicks, dip the banana slices in melted chocolate to create the phase of the moon you desire, e.g., last quarter (half-covered), crescent(one-third-covered), or even new moon (fully-covered)!
- Activity (Phases Booklet) - Have the students create a mini-booklet showing the phases of the moon. Use the information in the snack activity for the phases of the moon to include and let your students come up with the way they want to present each phase in their booklet.

Listen While You Eat

Reading Assignment

- *DK Children's Encyclopedia* pg. 171 (Moon)

Book Suggestions

- *Faces of the Moon* by Bob Crelin and Leslie Evans
- *The Moon Book* by Gail Gibbons
- *The Moon Seems to Change (Let's-Read-and-Find Out Science 2)* by Franklyn M. Branley and Barbara and Ed Emberley

Week 1 Notes

Week 2 Grid Schedule

Main Idea	
An astronaut is a person who travels to space.	
Supplies Needed	
Hands-on Projects	3 Balloons, Thick fabric (such as a woolen or fleece scarf), Thin fabric (such as a thin cotton T-shirt or pillowcase), Warm water
Coordinating Activities	Markers, Picture of the student's face, Freeze-dried (or dehydrated) food, Toilet paper

Weekly Schedule

	Day 1	Day 2	Day 3	Day 4
Lunch Items	❑ Make the astronaut science sandwich - read the meat, discuss the bread, and color the page.*	❑ Add some cheese to your sandwich with the hands-on project: Space Materials.*	❑ Read the *DK Children's Encyclopedia* pg. 31.	❑ Add some mayo to your sandwich with the coordinating activity: Spacesuit Design.
Feast Fillers	❑ Choose one or more of the library books to read.	❑ Add some more flavor with the coordinating activity: Astro-Food.	❑ Add some more spice with the coordinating activity: Toilet Paper Astronaut.	❑ Choose one or more of the library books to read.

** If you are short on time, these items will create a Bare-Bones Snack for your week.*

Week 2 List Schedule

Weekly Overview

Focus-of-the-Week

- An astronaut is a person who travels to space.

Supplies Needed

	Hands-on Project Materials
Hands-on Project Materials	3 Balloons, Thick fabric (such as a woolen or fleece scarf), Thin fabric (such as a thin cotton T-shirt or pillowcase), Warm water
Coordinating Activity Supplies	Markers, Picture of the student's face, Freeze-dried (or dehydrated) food, Toilet paper

Weekly Checklist

Bare-Bones Snack

- ☐ Make the astronaut science sandwich - read the meat, discuss the bread, and color the page.
- ☐ Add some cheese to your sandwich with the hands-on project: Space Materials.

Complete the Lunch

- ☐ Add some mayo to your sandwich with the coordinating activity: Spacesuit Design.
- ☐ Read the *DK Children's Encyclopedia* pg. 31.

Making it a Feast

- ☐ Add some more spice with the coordinating activity: Toilet Paper Astronaut.
- ☐ Add some more flavor with the coordinating activity: Astro-Food.
- ☐ Choose one or more of the library books to read.

Week 2: Astronauts

The Science Sandwich

The Meat

Read the following introduction to the students (LM pg. 102, RN pg. 48):

Did you know that there is no bread in space? That means that my dear friend and astronaut can't have a single sandwich while he is on the International Space Station.

It's a tough life for those guys. But when he gets back, Ulysses and I make him a giant Reuben sandwich – complete with corned beef and sauerkraut, dripping with melted Swiss and Russian dressing. He gobbles up that rye bread encased deliciousness like a starving man in the desert!

But we are not here to discuss an astronaut's sandwich preferences! We are here to talk about what astronauts do, but before I share – what do you think an astronaut does? (Pause to give time for the students to answer.)

Wow – that's an interesting job description! Astronauts are people who train for years and years so that they can take part in missions to space. Their job is to help us learn more about the universe. Sometimes they are in space for only a few days to do a quick repair job; sometimes they live in space for weeks to do research on the International Space Station.

Either way, when astronauts are in space, they have to wear a special space suit. These days, the space suit has a visor that protects their eyes from the sun, which is super strong out in space. It has places to attach the tools they need and a camera to record what they are doing. The space suit has a backpack with oxygen for breathing and water to help heat or cool the astronaut. It is made of many layers of fabric that help keep the astronaut safe and allow him or her to move about in space.

With all this stuff, the space suit is super heavy! It weighs around 300 pounds when it's all there, but that's okay because out in space, the astronaut is weightless, thanks to a lack of gravity.

Now it's your turn. Can you tell me about the kind of space suit you would design?

The Bread

Discussion Questions

- ☐ Ask the students the following questions:
  - **?** What do astronauts do?
  - **?** What is special about space that make astronauts weightless?

Written Assignments

- ☐ Have the students color the coloring page found on LM pg. 103.
- ☐ Have the students add what they have learned to the astronauts notes mini-book on RN pg. 49. Then, have them glue the mini-book into their journal.

Cheesy Additions

Scientific Demonstration – Space Materials

In this demonstration project, you and the students will test how different materials hold heat.

Materials Needed

- ✓ 3 Balloons
- ✓ Thick fabric (such as a woolen or fleece scarf)
- ✓ Thin fabric (such as a thin cotton T-shirt or pillowcase)
- ✓ Warm water

Steps to Complete

1. Say to the students, "Summer has asked us to learn a bit more about how different materials can hold heat. As scientists look at designing a space suit for astronauts, they need to consider how well the fabric holds in heat. We are going to look at a thicker fabric and a thinner fabric in this demonstration and then we'll record our findings in our lab manual for Summer and Ulysses to review later. Let's begin!"
2. Begin by filling the three balloons with warm water.
3. Then, have the students stuff a balloon into the thick fabric, wrap one in the thin fabric, and leave the other last balloon unprotected.
4. Have the students set all of the balloons on a shelf in the refrigerator.
5. After 15 minutes, have the students go feel each balloon to see how warm they are and have them record their observations on the demonstration sheet found on LM pg. 104 or on a chart you draw in their journal.

Results and Explanation

The students should see that the balloon inside the thick fabric stayed the warmest, while the ones covered with the thin fabric cooled off a bit, but was still warmer than the balloon that was exposed to the chill inside the fridge. This is because the materials used to make things like woolen hats or fleece scarfs traps heat efficiently, preventing the item inside from getting cooled off too quickly. The thinner fabric can also hold a bit of heat: not as much as the thick fabric, but more than nothing at all.

The Mayo and More

Coordinating Activities

- ✂ Art (Spacesuit Design) - Have the students create their own spacesuit and helmet on the body template on the activity sheet on LM pg. 105. When they are done, have them glue a picture of themselves on the black circle. You will need markers and a picture of the students face for this project.
- ✂ Snack (Astro-Food) - Get one or more types of freeze-dried (or dehydrated) food. Set the food out and explain to the students that astronauts often eat food that has been freeze-dried or dehydrated so that it will last longer. They usually rehydrate or heat it up in space, but today for snack you are going to try space food before it gets space-cooked!
- ✂ Activity (Toilet Paper Astronaut) - Have the students use a roll of toilet paper to make a "space suit." Then, have them perform tasks like picking up a pencil to see how their toilet paper suit affects their abilities.

Listen While You Eat

Reading Assignment

- *DK Children's Encyclopedia* pg. 31 (Astronauts)

Book Suggestions

- *If You Decide to Go to the Moon* by Faith McNulty and Steven Kellogg
- *DK Readers L2: Astronaut: Living in Space* by Deborah Lock
- *Floating in Space (Let's-Read-and-Find... Science 2)* by Franklyn M. Branley and True Kelley

Week 2 Notes

Week 3 Grid Schedule

<table>
<tr><th colspan="5">Main Idea</th></tr>
<tr><td colspan="5">Our solar system includes a group of planets and other objects all in orbit around the Sun.</td></tr>
<tr><th colspan="5">Supplies Needed</th></tr>
<tr><td>Hands-on Projects</td><td colspan="4">Labeled picture of our solar system (Appendix pg. 233), Blank solar system template (Appendix pg. 234), Pencil</td></tr>
<tr><td>Coordinating Activities</td><td colspan="4">Black crayon or chalk pastel, Picture of the Milky Way galaxy, Silver glitter, Glue, Different types of fruit, Elastic string, Different kinds of beads</td></tr>
<tr><th colspan="5">Weekly Schedule</th></tr>
<tr><th></th><th>Day 1</th><th>Day 2</th><th>Day 3</th><th>Day 4</th></tr>
<tr><td>Lunch Items</td><td>❑ Make the solar system science sandwich - read the meat, discuss the bread, and color the page.*</td><td>❑ Add some cheese to your sandwich with the hands-on project: Solar System Labels.*</td><td>❑ Read the DK Children's Encyclopedia pg. 167 or pg. 233.</td><td>❑ Add some mayo to your sandwich with the coordinating activity: Galaxy Art.</td></tr>
<tr><td>Feast Fillers</td><td>❑ Choose one or more of the library books to read.</td><td>❑ Add some more flavor with the coordinating activity: Fruity Solar System.</td><td>❑ Add some more spice with the coordinating activity: Solar System Bracelet.</td><td>❑ Choose one or more of the library books to read.</td></tr>
</table>

** If you are short on time, these items will create a Bare-Bones Snack for your week.*

Week 3 List Schedule

Weekly Overview

Focus-of-the-Week

- Our solar system includes a group of planets and other objects all in orbit around the Sun.

Supplies Needed

	Hands-on Project Materials
Hands-on Project Materials	Labeled picture of our solar system (Appendix pg. 233), Blank solar system template (Appendix pg. 234), Pencil
Coordinating Activity Supplies	Black crayon or chalk pastel, Picture of the Milky Way galaxy, Silver glitter, Glue, Different types of fruit, Elastic string, Different kinds of beads

Weekly Checklist

Bare-Bones Snack

- ❑ Make the solar system sandwich - read the meat, discuss the bread, and color the page.
- ❑ Add some cheese to your sandwich with the hands-on project: Solar System Labels.

Complete the Lunch

- ❑ Add some mayo to your sandwich with the coordinating activity: Galaxy Art.
- ❑ Read the *DK Children's Encyclopedia* pg. 167 and pg. 233.

Making it a Feast

- ❑ Add some more spice with the coordinating activity: Solar System Bracelet.
- ❑ Add some more flavor with the coordinating activity: Fruity Solar System.
- ❑ Choose one or more of the library books to read.

Week 3: Our Solar System

The Science Sandwich

The Meat

Read the following introduction to the students (LM pg. 106, RN pg. 50):

So, remember last week, when I said there was no bread in space? Well, there once was a sandwich in space! A long time ago, an astronaut from the Gemini 3 mission thought it would be a good idea to smuggle his favorite sandwich into space in his flight suit.

Once out there, he took a out and it turned out to be not quite as delectable in outer space as it was on Earth. It turned out to cause quite the hullabaloo and a lot of today's space cuisine rules are there because of that single corned-beef-sandwich smuggle.

But we are not here to discuss space food; we are here today to talk about the solar system. Before I share some cool facts, can you tell me what you know about our solar system? (Pause to give time for the students to answer.)

Alrighty then! Our solar system is located on an arm of the Milky Way galaxy. It is the collection of planets and other objects that orbit around the sun, which is at the very center.

Our solar system has eight major planets – Mercury, Venus, Earth, Mars, Jupiter, Saturn, Uranus, and Neptune – and several dwarf planets, including Pluto. Pluto was once considered a planet, until astronomers came together and created a better definition of what a planet is – it caused quite the uproar back in my day.

Our solar system also includes comets, stars, asteroids, and any other kind of space debris, like satellites, that orbit around the sun. To us here on Earth, our solar system seems huge. But really, it's one small part of a galaxy that is one small part of a massive universe!

Now it's your turn. Can you point out the sun in our solar system? Remember, it's at the center. Can you point to one of the planets? Which one do you think is Earth?

(***Note** – You can read more about the ill-fated corned beef space sandwich in the following article: https://airandspace.si.edu/stories/editorial/how-astronaut-smuggled-sandwich-space.*)

The Bread

Discussion Questions

- ☐ Ask the students the following questions:
  - **?** Can you name some of thing things our solar system includes?

Written Assignment

- ☐ Have the students color the coloring page found on LM pg. 107.
- ☐ Have the students add what they have learned to the volcano notes mini-book on RN pg. 51. Then, have them glue the mini-book into their journal.

Cheesy Additions

Scientific Demonstration – Solar System Labels

In this demonstration project, you and the students will see a small scale version of our solar system.

Materials Needed

- ✓ Labeled picture of our solar system (Appendix pg. 234)
- ✓ Blank solar system template (Appendix pg. 233 or LM pg. 108)
- ✓ Pencil (or pre-written labels from Appendix pg. 233)

Steps to Complete

1. Say to the students, "Today, Summer has asked us to label a drawing of the solar system for our own home lab. She and Ulysses have already provide a picture for us, and we are going to review the eight planets, plus one dwarf planet, in our solar system. We'll add labels for these on the picture in our lab manual for Summer and Ulysses to review later. Let's get started!"
2. Turn to the page in the lab manual (pg. 108) with the solar system or give the students a copy of the template from the appendix (pg. 233).
3. Show the students the labeled picture of our solar system. We have provided one for you in the Appendix on pg. 234 or you can use the one found in the *DK Children's Encyclopedia* on page 233. (***Note** - Pluto is not included in the picture found in the encyclopedia.*)
4. Work together to identify and label the eight planets (Mercury, Venus, Earth, Mars, Jupiter, Saturn, Uranus, and Neptune) and one dwarf planet (Pluto) on the solar system picture on the demonstration sheet on LM pg. 108 or in their journal.

Results and Explanation

The students should become a bit more familiar with the planets in our solar system and gain an understanding of how close or how far away they are from the sun.

The Mayo and More

Coordinating Activities

✂ Art (Galaxy Art) - Have the students make a picture representing the galaxy our solar system is found in, the Milky Way. You will need the following supplies: black crayon or chalk pastel, picture of the Milky Way galaxy, silver glitter, and glue. Have the students make their own Milky Way drawing using the crayon or pastel on LM pg. 109 or in their journal. Then, have them trace the lines with glue and sprinkle silver glitter over it. Shake off the excess glitter and let the creations dry.

- ✂ Snack (Fruity Solar System) - Make a fruit version of the solar system. You will need different types of fruit to represent the planets and the sun. You can see an example of this at the following website:
  - https://meandbmaketea.com/2016/03/14/fruity-solar-system/
- ✂ Activity (Solar System Bracelet) - Have the students make a solar system bracelet. You will need elastic string and different kinds of beads. Directions for this project can be found at the following website:
  - http://formontana.net/bracelet2.html

Listen While You Eat

Reading Assignment

- *DK Children's Encyclopedia* pg. 167 (Milky Way), pg. 233 (Solar System)

Book Suggestions

- *There's No Place Like Space: All About Our Solar System (Cat in the Hat's Learning Library)* by Tish Rabe and Aristides Ruiz
- *Scholastic Reader Level 2: Solar System* by Gregory Vogt
- *The Planets in Our Solar System (Let's-Read-and-Find Out Science)* by Franklyn M. Branley and Kevin O'Malley

Week 3 Notes

Week 4 Grid Schedule

Main Idea				
Stars form pictures in the sky called constellations.				
Supplies Needed				
Hands-on Projects	Foil, Toilet Paper Tube, Pin, Small flashlight, Constellation pictures (Appendix pg. 235), Rubber band, Sharpie marker			
Coordinating Activities	Gold star stickers, White crayon, Paper, Dark blue paint, Plain cupcakes, Blue and yellow frosting			
Weekly Schedule				
	Day 1	**Day 2**	**Day 3**	**Day 4**
Lunch Items	❑ Make the constellation science sandwich - read the meat, discuss the bread, and color the page.*	❑ Add some cheese to your sandwich with the hands-on project: Flashlight Planetarium.*	❑ Read the *DK Children's Encyclopedia* pg. 73.	❑ Add some mayo to your sandwich with the coordinating activity: Constellation Resist.
Feast Fillers	❑ Choose one or more of the library books to read.	❑ Add some more flavor with the coordinating activity: Orion Cupcakes.	❑ Add some more spice with the coordinating activity: Night Sky Spotting.	❑ Choose one or more of the library books to read.

** If you are short on time, these items will create a Bare-Bones Snack for your week.*

Week 4 List Schedule

Weekly Overview

Focus-of-the-Week

- Stars form pictures in the sky called constellations.

Supplies Needed

	Hands-on Project Materials
Hands-on Project Materials	Foil, Toilet Paper Tube, Pin, Small flashlight, Constellation pictures (Appendix pg. 235), Rubber band, Sharpie marker
Coordinating Activity Supplies	Gold star stickers, White crayon, Paper, Dark blue paint, Plain cupcakes, Blue and yellow frosting

Weekly Checklist

Bare-Bones Snack

- ❑ Make the constellation science sandwich - read the meat, discuss the bread, and color the page.
- ❑ Add some cheese to your sandwich with the hands-on project: Flashlight Planetarium.

Complete the Lunch

- ❑ Add some mayo to your sandwich with the coordinating activity: Constellation Resist.
- ❑ Read the *DK Children's Encyclopedia* pg. 73.

Making it a Feast

- ❑ Add some more spice with the coordinating activity: Night Sky Spotting.
- ❑ Add some more flavor with the coordinating activity: Orion Cupcakes.
- ❑ Choose one or more of the library books to read.

Week 4: Stars

The Science Sandwich

The Meat

Read the following introduction to the students (LM pg. 110, RN pg. 52):

On a clear night, Ulysses and I like to take our French dip sandwiches outside. The warm roast beef and melted cheese blend with the savory beef consommé as we enjoy an incredible scene.

We dunk until our hearts are content, staring up at the pictures painted on the canvas of the night sky. It's as close as we get to visiting a museum during our busier times.

There is peace in filling your belly with a simple, warm meal as you gaze at the same stars people have been looking at for hundreds of years. But we are not here to chat about how Ulysses and I unwind – we are here to talk about constellations.

What do you know about constellations or stars? (Pause to give time for the students to answer.)

You are one smart cookie! When we look up at the night sky, all those white dots we see are stars. Stars are really giant balls of exploding gas, but they are so far away from us that they look like tiny, pinpricks of light. The closest star to our planet is actually the sun!

In the days before GPS and maps on our phones, people used to use the stars to navigate or find their way. To make this easier, they gave groups or patterns in the stars, names. These constellations were named after heroes, animals, and other familiar objects.

Today, we have 88 named constellations, or groups of stars that form pictures in the sky. Some are easy to spot, like the Big Dipper and Orion's belt. Some are a bit harder to find, like Cygnus the Swan, which you can see on your sheet. But the longer you observe, the more you will see!

Now it's your turn. Have you ever seen a star picture, otherwise known as a constellation, in the night sky?

The Bread

Discussion Questions

- ☐ Ask the students the following questions:
  - **?** What is a star?
  - **?** What is a constellation?

Written Assignment

- [ ] Have the students color the coloring page found on LM pg. 111.
- [ ] Have the students add what they have learned to the fossil notes mini-book on RN pg. 53. Then, have them glue the mini-book into their journal.

Cheesy Additions

Scientific Demonstration – Flashlight Planetarium

In this demonstration project, you and the students will see several of the constellations.

Materials Needed

- ✓ Foil
- ✓ Toilet Paper Tube
- ✓ Pin
- ✓ Small flashlight
- ✓ Constellation pictures (Appendix pg. 235)
- ✓ Rubber band
- ✓ Sharpie marker

Steps to Complete

1. Say to the students, "Summer has asked that we create a small, indoor picture of the constellations that we can use to view them anytime we like, even during the day! Then, we'll take a picture of what we create and put it in our lab manual for her and Ulysses to review later. Let's get started!"
2. Have the students tear the foil into six squares so that each square will fit around the end of the toilet paper tube and have enough leftover material to be secured by the rubber band.
3. Hand the students a copy of the constellation pictures from the Appendix on pg. 235. Have them use a pin and the constellation pictures to create six foil constellations to use in their flashlight planetarium. Write the name of constellation in the bottom corner of each piece of foil for them using the Sharpie marker.
4. Once they have all six constellations, head into a room with no windows.
5. Have the students view each constellation by placing the foil template at one end of the toilet paper tube so that the constellation is centered in the middle of the tube. Then, secure the foil in place using the rubber band. Next, set the tube on a desk and place the flashlight in the other end of the tube and aim the foil end of the tube toward a wall. Finally, turn off the lights and turn on the flashlights to view the constellations!
6. Have the students take a picture or draw on on LM pg. 112 and add their observations.

Results and Explanation

The students should see the star pictures on the wall of the darkened room. If you would like to explore the stories behind these constellations, we recommend the following resource: *The Stars and Their Stories by Alice Griffith.* (Note – This book can be downloaded for free from Archive.org at the following link: https://archive.org/details/starsandtheirst00unkngoog.)

The Mayo and More

Coordinating Activities

- Art (Constellation Resist) - Have the students make a constellation model using resist painting on LM pg. 113 or in their journal. You will need gold star stickers, white crayon, paper, and dark blue paint. Have them make the outline of the Big Dipper constellation from the workshop pictures, using the star stickers and white crayon. After they have done this, have them paint all over it with the dark blue paint. Once the paint is dry, have the students remove the star stickers to reveal their full constellations.
- Snack (Orion Cupcakes) - Make your favorite cupcake recipe and frost the cupcakes with blue frosting. Then use yellow frosting to draw the outline of the Orion constellation. (*This is the constellation picture on the week's coloring page on LM pg. 111 and on the reference notes mini-book cover on pg. 53.*)
- Activity (Night Sky Spotting) - Take the students outside just after dark to look at the night sky. Here are a few tips:
  - https://elementalscience.com/blogs/podcast/episode-9

Listen While You Eat

Reading Assignment

- *DK Children's Encyclopedia* pg. 73 (Constellations)

Book Suggestions

- *Glow in the Dark Constellations*
- *The Sky Is Full of Stars (Let's-Read-and-Find... Science 2)* by Franklyn M. Branley and Felicia Bond
- *The Big Dipper (Let's-Read-and-Find... Science 1)* by Franklyn M. Branley and Molly Coxe
- *Circus in the Sky (Kids)* by Nancy Guettier

Week 4 Notes

SUMMER'S LAB
UNIT 7: MATTER

Unit 7 At-A-Glance

Unit Purpose

This unit is your student's first look at the world of chemistry. In this unit, the students will learn the basics of matter and how it behaves.

Matter Topics

- ✓ Week 1: Atoms
- ✓ Week 2: Solids and Liquids
- ✓ Week 3: Freezing and Melting
- ✓ Week 4: Solutions and Mixtures

Supplies Needed

Week	Hands-on Project Materials	Coordinating Activity Supplies
1	4 Pipe cleaners, Round beads in three different colors (at least 3 of each color)	Paint, Sugar cookies, White icing, 3 Colors of M&M's
2	Various liquids and solids from around the house (such as ice, crayons, LEGO blocks, dish soap, water, or juice)	Magazines for pictures, Popsicles, 3 Balloons, Ice, Water
3	Small paper cup, Water, Plate	Food coloring, Water, Ice-cube tray, A variety of fruits and vegetables
4	Glass jar, Pipe cleaner, String, Pencil, Water, Borax	Epsom salts, Warm water, Glass, Food coloring, Paintbrush, 6 Cups, Eyedropper

Week 1 Grid Schedule

Main Idea	
Atoms are the building blocks of matter.	
Supplies Needed	
Hands-on Projects	4 Pipe cleaners, Round beads in three different colors (at least 3 of each color)
Coordinating Activities	Paint, Sugar cookies, White icing, 3 Colors of M&M's

Weekly Schedule

	Day 1	Day 2	Day 3	Day 4
Lunch Items	❑ Make the atom science sandwich - read the meat, discuss the bread, and color the page.*	❑ Add some cheese to your sandwich with the hands-on project: Model Atom.*	❑ Read the *DK Children's Encyclopedia* pg. 34	❑ Add some mayo to your sandwich with the coordinating activity: Fingerprint Atom.
Feast Fillers	❑ Choose one or more of the library books to read.	❑ Add some more flavor with the coordinating activity: Atom Cookies.	❑ Add some more spice with the coordinating activity: Atoms and Isotopes Game.	❑ Choose one or more of the library books to read.

** If you are short on time, this item will create a Bare-Bones Snack for your week.*

Week 1 List Schedule

Weekly Overview

Focus-of-the-Week

- Atoms are the building blocks of matter.

Supplies Needed

	Hands-on Project Materials
Hands-on Project Materials	4 Pipe cleaners, Round beads in three different colors (at least 3 of each color)
Coordinating Activity Supplies	Paint, Sugar cookies, White icing, 3 Colors of M&M's

Weekly Checklist

Bare-Bones Snack

- ❑ Make the atom science sandwich - read the meat, discuss the bread, and color the page.
- ❑ Add some cheese to your sandwich with the hands-on project: Model Atom.

Complete the Lunch

- ❑ Add some mayo to your sandwich with the coordinating activity: Fingerprint Atom.
- ❑ Read the *DK Children's Encyclopedia* pg. 34.

Making it a Feast

- ❑ Add some more spice with the coordinating activity: Atoms and Isotopes Game.
- ❑ Add some more flavor with the coordinating activity: Atom Cookies.
- ❑ Choose one or more of the library books to read.

Week 1: Atoms

The Science Sandwich

The Meat

Read the following introduction to the students (LM pg. 116, RN pg. 54):

One of my favorite snacks at teatime is a ham, brie, and apple finger sandwich. Ulysses prefers a peanut butter and bacon tea sandwich, which I haven't had the chutzpah to try . . . yet.

Anywhoo, these tiny sandwiches hit the spot when it comes to an afternoon snack. Each one contains all the important keys of a full sandwich, just in a smaller package. And right now, you are thinking "That's nice, but what in the world do tea sandwiches have to do with chemistry."

Well, quite a lot – but that's not the point. The point is that we are here today to chat about atoms, but before I share what I know, have you ever heard of an atom before? (Pause to give time for the students to answer.)

Oh, fantastic! So, the tea sandwich is the smallest sandwich and the atom is the tiny unit that builds everything around us. See the connection? Yeah, it is a bit of a stretch . . . but seriously, the atom is super tiny! It's so small that you can't see it with your bare eyes. You have to use something that magnifies it, or rather makes it much, much bigger.

Even though scientists couldn't see atoms, the idea that they existed has been around for hundreds of years. They believed that all matter – in other words, everything – was composed of tiny particles and they called those specks atoms.

Nowadays, we know that atoms have a central core called a nucleus that contains protons and neutrons. And that atoms have electrons whizzing around the outside of the core. These electrons, protons, and neutrons are called subatomic particles.

Atoms have an equal number of protons and electrons. If they don't, we call them ions. And typically, atoms of the same type will have the same number of protons and neutrons. If they don't, we call these isotopes!

Now it's your turn. Can you point out the nucleus in the atom on the page? Can you point out the electrons?

The Bread

Discussion Questions

- ☐ Ask the students the following questions:
  - **?** What are atoms?
  - **?** Where can you find the protons and neutrons in the atom?
  - **?** Where can you find the electrons in the atom?

Written Assignments

- ☐ Have the students color the coloring page found on LM pg. 117.
- ☐ Have the students add what they have learned to atoms notes mini-book on RN pg. 55. Then, have them glue the mini-book into their journal.

Cheesy Additions

Scientific Demonstration - Model Atom

In this demonstration project, you and the students will see what an atom looks like.

Materials Needed

- ✓ 4 Pipe cleaners
- ✓ Round beads in three different colors (at least 3 of each color)

Steps to Complete

1. Gather up the supplies needed to begin this project.
2. Say to the students, "Summer has asked us to make a model of the atom that we can see and play with! We are going to use these beads to represent the subatomic particles - the electrons, protons, and neutrons. Then, we'll use the pipe cleaners to hold them all in place. Let's begin!"
3. Have the students select which beads will be electrons, protons, and neutrons.
4. Next, have them string three protons beads and three neutrons beads on one of the pipe cleaners, alternating between the two. Once done, have the students wrap the this portion of the pipe cleaner into a ball to form a nucleus, leaving a straight end to connect to the electron rings they will make in the next step.
5. Then, have the students place one electron bead on a pipe cleaner and twist the pipe cleaner closed to form a ring. Repeat this process two more times, so that they have 3 electron rings.
6. Finally, fit the rings inside each other and then hang the nucleus ball in the center, using the pipe cleaner tail left in step two to attach the nucleus and hold the rings together. (*See image for reference.*)
7. Have the students take a picture of their atoms or draw their models on the demonstration sheet on LM pg. 118 or to their journal.

Results and Explanation

The students should see be able to visualize an atom, even though they are too small to see with the naked eye.

The Mayo and More

Coordinating Activities

- Art (Fingerprint Atom) - Have the students use their fingers to add the subatomic particles (electrons, protons, and neutrons) on the activity sheet on LM pg. 119. You will need three colors of paints, one for each subatomic particle. When the students create their atom, make sure that they use the same number of fingerprints for each of the particles. The electrons should be on the lines, while the protons and neutrons should be in a cluster at the center.
- Snack (Atom Cookies) - Make some atomic cookies with your students using a sugar cookie, white icing, and three different colors of M&M's. See the following website for directions:
  - http://technoprairie.blogspot.com/2009/02/atomic-cookies.html
- Activity (Atoms and Isotopes Game) - Have the students play an atoms and isotopes game. You can get directions for this game from the following blog post:
  - http://elementalscience.com/blogs/science-activities/60317571-free-chemistry-game

Listen while you eat

Reading Assignment

- *DK Children's Encyclopedia* pg. 34 (Atoms)

Book Suggestions

- *What Are Atoms? (Rookie Read-About Science)* by Lisa Trumbauer
- *Atoms and Molecules (Building Blocks of Matter)* by Richard and Louise Spilsbury
- *Atoms (Simply Science)* by Melissa Stewart

Week 1 Notes

Week 2 Grid Schedule

Main Idea	
Liquid water can move, but solid water keeps its shape.	
Supplies Needed	
Hands-on Projects	Various liquids and solids from around the house (such as ice, crayons, LEGO blocks, dish soap, water, or juice)
Coordinating Activities	Magazines for pictures, Popsicles, 3 Balloons, Ice, Water

Weekly Schedule				
	Day 1	**Day 2**	**Day 3**	**Day 4**
Lunch Items	❑ Make the liquids and solids science sandwich - read the meat, discuss the bread, and color the page.*	❑ Add some cheese to your sandwich with the hands-on project: Is it liquid or solid?*	❑ Read the *DK Children's Encyclopedia* pg. 148 and pg. 234.	❑ Add some mayo to your sandwich with the coordinating activity: Liquid-Solid Collage.
Feast Fillers	❑ Choose one or more of the library books to read.	❑ Add some more flavor with the coordinating activity: Solid Popsicles.	❑ Add some more spice with the coordinating activity: States of Matter Balloons.	❑ Choose one or more of the library books to read.

** If you are short on time, these items will create a Bare-Bones Snack for your week.*

Week 2 List Schedule

Weekly Overview

Focus-of-the-Week

- Liquid water can move, but solid water keeps its shape.

Supplies Needed

	Hands-on Project Materials
Hands-on Project Materials	Various liquids and solids from around the house (such as ice, crayons, LEGO blocks, dish soap, water, or juice)
Coordinating Activity Supplies	Magazines for pictures, Popsicles, 3 Balloons, Ice, Water

Weekly Checklist

Bare-Bones Snack

- ❑ Make the liquids and solids science sandwich - read the meat, discuss the bread, and color the page.
- ❑ Add some cheese to your sandwich with the hands-on project: Is it liquid or solid?

Complete the Lunch

- ❑ Add some mayo to your sandwich with the coordinating activity: Liquid-Solid Collage.
- ❑ Read the *DK Children's Encyclopedia* pg. 148 and pg. 234.

Making it a Feast

- ❑ Add some more spice with the coordinating activity: States of Matter Balloons.
- ❑ Add some more flavor with the coordinating activity: Solid Popsicles.
- ❑ Choose one or more of the library books to read.

Week 2: Liquids and Solids

The Science Sandwich

The Meat

Read the following introduction to the students (LM pg. 120, RN pg. 56):

Let's say you set a piece of bread on a plate and top it with a slice of bologna. Then, you unwrap a square of cheese and place it on the bologna. Maybe you add a bit of tomato or some mayonnaise before you cover it all with another piece of bread.

You step back and stare at the bologna sandwich on the plate in front of you. Does it move on its own? No, it does not.

And the reason for that can be explained with science! It all has to do with the states of matter, but before I explain all that – what do you know about liquids and solids? (Pause to give time for the students to answer.)

Hmm, that is very interesting! Both liquids and solids are what we call states of matter. These are ways that matter, or things, can be. It has quite a bit to do with the movement of the atoms inside the object, but we won't get into all that right now.

Let's go back to your bologna sandwich, which is a solid. Your bologna has a first name, wait that's not right . . . your bologna sandwich will not move on its own. It stays in the same place you left it until you touch it again. This is because solids keep their shape.

Now let's say you have a glass of lemonade with your sandwich. And, oops, your clumsy sibling bumps your glass and it tips over. The lemonade spills everywhere! Why? Because lemonade is a liquid and liquids move, taking shape of the container they are in. When a liquid leaves a container, it spreads out everywhere, moving without any of your help.

That's a super simple way of looking at the two states of matter – solids and liquids. There are two more states – gas and plasma – but we'll save those for future studies.

For right now, it's your turn. Can you look at the picture and point to the solid ice? How about the liquid water?

The Bread

Discussion Questions

- ☐ Ask the students the following questions:
  - **?** What is a solid?
  - **?** What is a liquid?
  - **?** Can you name at least two of the states of matter?

Written Assignments

- ☐ Have the students color the coloring page found on LM pg. 121.
- ☐ Have the students add what they have learned to the liquids and solids notes mini-book on RN pg. 57. Then, have them glue the mini-book into their journal.

Cheesy Additions

Scientific Demonstration – Is it liquid or solid?

In this demonstration project, you and the students will explore liquids and solids that can be found in your home.

Materials Needed

- ✓ Various liquids and solids from around the house (such as ice, crayons, LEGO blocks, dish soap, water, or juice)

Steps to Complete

1. Say to the students, "Summer has asked us to learn a bit more about the solids and liquids we can find in our house. Remember that solids keep their shape, while liquids move freely when not in a container. We are going to look at each of these materials from our house and categorize them as liquid or solid. Then, we'll record our findings in our lab manual for Summer and Ulysses to review later. Let's begin!"
2. Begin by setting out the various liquid and solid materials you collected from around the house.
3. Allow the students to observe the materials. You can ask them the following questions:
   - ? What happens when you touch the material?
   - ? Does the material change shape?
4. Then, have the students write down the name of the material on the chart on the demonstration sheet found on LM pg. 122 or on a chart you draw in their journal. Have them circle whether the material is a liquid or solid.

Results and Explanation

The students should be able to identify which are the liquids and which are the solids from the household items.

The Mayo and More

Coordinating Activities

- ✂ Art (Liquid-Solid Collage) - Have the students make a collage for both liquids and solids using pictures from magazines. For example, you can add pictures of milk gallons or glasses of juice for the liquids side and pictures of furniture or food on the solids side. Have the students glue the pictures on the activity page on LM pg. 123 or in their journal.

- Snack (Solid Popsicle) - Point out to your student that popsicles are solids. As they eat the popsicle, ask them what happens to the solid popsicle in their mouth? (*It melts into a liquid.*)
- Activity (States of Matter Balloons) - You will need 3 balloons, several ice cubes, and some water. Fill one balloon with the ice cubes, one with some water, and one with air. Have the students observe the balloons and discuss with them how the different states of matter feel.

Listen While You Eat

Reading Assignment

- *DK Children's Encyclopedia* pg. 148 (Liquids) and pg. 234 (Solids)

Book Suggestions

- *Solids, Liquids, and Gases (Rookie Read-About Science)* by Ginger Garrett
- *What Is the World Made Of? All About Solids, Liquids, and Gases (Let's-Read-and-Find Out Science, Stage 2)* by Kathleen Weidner Zoehfeld and Paul Meisel

Week 2 Notes

Week 3 Grid Schedule

Main Idea				
Freezing is when a liquid is chilled and turns into solid. Melting is when a solid is heated up and turns into a liquid.				
Supplies Needed				
Hands-on Projects	Small paper cup, Water, Plate			
Coordinating Activities	Food coloring, Water, Ice-cube tray, A variety of fruits and vegetables			
Weekly Schedule				
	Day 1	**Day 2**	**Day 3**	**Day 4**
Lunch Items	❑ Make the freezing and melting science sandwich - read the meat, discuss the bread, and color the page.*	❑ Add some cheese to your sandwich with the hands-on project: Changes in State.*	❑ Read the *DK Children's Encyclopedia* pg. 268.	❑ Add some mayo to your sandwich with the coordinating activity: Ice Painting.
Feast Fillers	❑ Choose one or more of the library books to read.	❑ Add some more flavor with the coordinating activity: Frozen Foods.	❑ Add some more spice with the coordinating activity: Freeze Tag.	❑ Choose one or more of the library books to read.

** If you are short on time, these items will create a Bare-Bones Snack for your week.*

Week 3 List Schedule

Weekly Overview

Focus-of-the-Week

- Freezing is when a liquid is chilled and turns into solid. Melting is when a solid is heated up and turns into a liquid.

Supplies Needed

	Hands-on Project Materials
Hands-on Project Materials	Small paper cup, Water, Plate
Coordinating Activity Supplies	Food coloring, Water, Ice-cube tray, A variety of fruits and vegetables

Weekly Checklist

Bare-Bones Snack

- ❑ Make the freezing and melting sandwich - read the meat, discuss the bread, and color the page.
- ❑ Add some cheese to your sandwich with the hands-on project: Changes in State.

Complete the Lunch

- ❑ Add some mayo to your sandwich with the coordinating activity: Ice Painting.
- ❑ Read the *DK Children's Encyclopedia* pg. 57.

Making it a Feast

- ❑ Add some more spice with the coordinating activity: Freeze Tag.
- ❑ Add some more flavor with the coordinating activity: Frozen Foods.
- ❑ Choose one or more of the library books to read.

Week 3: Freezing and Melting

The Science Sandwich

The Meat

Read the following introduction to the students (LM pg. 124, RN pg. 58):

On a hot summer day, Ulysses and I like to wrap up our meal with an ice cream sandwich. Ulysses prefers the standard version, while I love a good Neapolitan ice cream sandwiches!

The only bad thing about ice cream sandwiches is that on a hot day you have to gobble them up fast . . . well, maybe that's not such a bad thing! I bet you can tell me why . . . (Pause to give time for the students to answer.)

Yep! We have to gobble up our ice cream sandwiches on a hot day because if we don't, they will melt. And nobody likes a melty, mushy ice cream sandwich!

Well, our little hot-day-ice-cream snafu can be explained with science. You see, as the ice cream sandwich heats up, the tiny stuff inside, the stuff that makes up the ice cream, starts to heat up and move around faster. This causes our ice cream to go from a solid to a liquid and we call the process melting.

Now, let's say we realized our ice cream sandwich was starting to melt and ran inside to put it in the freezer. After about 10 minutes or so, we could pull it out and all the ice cream would be solid and firm once more. This is because, in the freezer, the tiny stuff inside cools down and basically stops moving. The ice cream in our sandwich has gone from a near liquid to a firm solid and we call this process freezing.

In short, melting is when a solid is heated up and turns into a liquid. Freezing is when a liquid is chilled and turns into solid.

Now it's your turn. Can you show me which way is melting? (Students should point from the ice to the water.) Can you show me which way is freezing? (Students should point from the water to the ice.)

The Bread

Discussion Questions

- ☐ Ask the students the following questions:
  - **?** What happens when a solid melts?
  - **?** What happens when a liquid freezes?

Written Assignment

- ☐ Have the students color the coloring page found on LM pg. 125.
- ☐ Have the students add what they have learned to the freezing and melting notes mini-book on RN pg. 59. Then, have them glue the mini-book into their journal.

Cheesy Additions

Scientific Demonstration - Changes in State

In this demonstration project, you and the students will observe what happens with liquid water freezes and when it melts.

Materials Needed

- ✓ Small paper cup
- ✓ Water
- ✓ Plate

Steps to Complete

1. Say to the students, "Today, Summer has asked us to observe what water is like when it freezes and what water is like when it melts. Let's get started!"
2. Fill the small paper cup about a third of the way with water. Place the cup into the freezer and wait for an hour.
3. After an hour, take the cup out of the freezer. Pop the frozen water (a.k.a. ice) onto the plate and let the students play with and observe it. You can ask the following questions to help:
   - ? How does the frozen water feel?
   - ? How does the frozen water smell?
   - ? What color is the frozen water?
4. Have the students add their observations to the demonstration sheet on LM pg. 126 or in their journal.
5. After they are done, wait about thirty minutes for the ice to melt. Once more, let the students play with and observe the melted water. You can ask the following questions to help:
   - ? How does the melted water feel?
   - ? How does the melted water smell?
   - ? What color is the melted water?
6. Have the students add their observations to the demonstration sheet

Results and Explanation

The students should see that the frozen water feels cold and hard, plus it moves only when touched. They should observe that the melted water feels warmer and will flow much more easily on the plate.

The Mayo and More

Coordinating Activities

- ✂ Art (Ice Paint) - Ahead of time, use food coloring or several drops of paint to make different colors of water. Freeze this colored water into cubes. Once they are frozen, let the students paint with the colored ice cubes on LM pg. 127 or in their journal.
- ✂ Snack (Frozen Foods) - Ahead of time, freeze some of the students' favorite fruits or vegetables (i.e., peas, corn, carrots, grapes, strawberries, or bananas, you could also freeze their favorite cookies or crackers). Serve the frozen food for snack. Have the students taste each one and talk about how it tastes the same and how it tastes different.
- ✂ Activity (Freeze Tag) - Have the students play a game of freeze tag. To add in melting to the game, have the tagged players shout "freeze" the first time they are tagged and "melt" when they are tagged a second time to be unfrozen.

Listen while you eat

Reading Assignment

- *DK Children's Encyclopedia* pg. 57 (Changing States)

Book Suggestions

- *Change It!: Solids, Liquids, Gases and You* by Adrienne Mason and Claudia Davila
- *Melting and Freezing: Matter (Science Readers: A Closer Look)* by Lisa Greathouse
- *Freezing and Melting (First Step Nonfiction)* by Robin Nelson

Week 3 Notes

Week 4 Grid Schedule

<table>
<tr><th colspan="5">Main Idea</th></tr>
<tr><td colspan="5">A mixture is a combination of solids or liquids. A solution is a mixture where a solid is dissolved in a liquid.</td></tr>
<tr><th colspan="5">Supplies Needed</th></tr>
<tr><td>Hands-on Projects</td><td colspan="4">Glass jar, Pipe cleaner, String, Pencil, Water, Borax</td></tr>
<tr><td>Coordinating Activities</td><td colspan="4">Epsom salts, Warm water, Glass, Food coloring, Paintbrush, 6 Cups, Eyedropper</td></tr>
<tr><th colspan="5">Weekly Schedule</th></tr>
<tr><td></td><td>Day 1</td><td>Day 2</td><td>Day 3</td><td>Day 4</td></tr>
<tr><td>Lunch Items</td><td>❑ Make the mixture and solution science sandwich - read the meat, discuss the bread, and color the page.*</td><td>❑ Add some cheese to your sandwich with the hands-on project: Crystal Solutions.*</td><td>❑ Read the DK Children's Encyclopedia pg. 168.</td><td>❑ Add some mayo to your sandwich with the coordinating activity: Solution Painting.</td></tr>
<tr><td>Feast Fillers</td><td>❑ Choose one or more of the library books to read.</td><td>❑ Add some more flavor with the coordinating activity: Mixture Sandwiches and Solution Drinks.</td><td>❑ Add some more spice with the coordinating activity: Color Mixing.</td><td>❑ Choose one or more of the library books to read.</td></tr>
</table>

** If you are short on time, these items will create a Bare-Bones Snack for your week.*

Week 4 List Schedule

Weekly Overview

Focus-of-the-Week

- A mixture is a combination of solids or liquids. A solution is a mixture where a solid is dissolved in a liquid.

Supplies Needed

	Hands-on Project Materials
Hands-on Project Materials	Glass jar, Pipe cleaner, String, Pencil, Water, Borax
Coordinating Activity Supplies	Epsom salts, Warm water, Glass, Food coloring, Paintbrush, 6 Cups, Eyedropper

Weekly Checklist

Bare-Bones Snack

- ❑ Make the mixtures and solutions science sandwich - read the meat, discuss the bread, and color the page.
- ❑ Add some cheese to your sandwich with the hands-on project: Crystal Solutions

Complete the Lunch

- ❑ Add some mayo to your sandwich with the coordinating activity: Solution Painting.
- ❑ Read the *DK Children's Encyclopedia* pg. 168.

Making it a Feast

- ❑ Add some more spice with the coordinating activity: Color Mixing.
- ❑ Add some more flavor with the coordinating activity: Mixture Sandwich and Solution Drinks.
- ❑ Choose one or more of the library books to read.

Week 4: Mixtures and Solutions

The Science Sandwich

The Meat

Read the following introduction to the students (LM pg. 128, RN pg. 60):

Hummus, roasted red peppers, and sprouts in a wrap. Ham and swiss cheese on rye. Salami, provolone, and cucumbers on French bread.

All these sandwiches are a combination of delicious ingredients with a "breadish" delivery system. These sandwiches are not only tasty, they are mixtures.

The soda or lemonade you drink with your sandwich is special type of mixture called a solution. Before I explain what mixtures or solutions are, do you know anything about these? (Pause to give time for the students to answer.)

Ahh, mixtures and solutions are big topics from chemistry. And after we finish today, you are going to be able to impress so many adults with your knowledge!

A mixture is a combination of solids, liquids, or gases – in other words, it's a combination of matter. Mixtures can be easily separated back into their original parts by sifting or filtering. But some mixtures, known as solutions, have substances dissolved in a liquid. These mixtures can be separated by evaporation.

Mixtures are easy to figure out, but for a solution let's think of how we make lemonade. You start by pouring some lemon juice, or if you are really industrious you squeeze a few lemons, into a pitcher. Then, you add a bit of sugar to the juice. You stir, stir, stir until the sugar crystals disappear. And to top it all off you add some water, creating some delicious lemonade. And my guess is that you had no idea that what you were making was a chemical solution!

Clear as muddy water? Which, by the way, is a another mixture - one that we can filter all that mud out of . . . eventually! Now it's your turn – grab a few lemons and a spot of sugar, or your favorite Kool-aid powder, and mix up a solution! Or a bowl, some sand, and a few Lego bricks to make a mixture you can sift!

The Bread

Discussion Questions

- ☐ Ask the students the following questions:
  - **?** What is a mixture?
  - **?** What is a solution?

Written Assignment

- ☐ Have the students color the coloring page found on LM pg. 129.
- ☐ Have the students add what they have learned to the mixture notes mini-book on RN pg. 61. Then, have them glue the mini-book into their journal.

Cheesy Additions

Scientific Demonstration - Crystal Solutions

In this demonstration project, you and the students will make a solution and then watch crystals form from that solution.

Materials Needed

- ✓ Glass jar
- ✓ Pipe cleaner
- ✓ String
- ✓ Pencil
- ✓ Water
- ✓ Borax

Steps to Complete

1. Say to the students, "Summer has asked us to make a solution and then let that solution sit and make crystals in our lab! We'll start by making a solution. Then, with a bit of time and patience, we'll watch as crystals form. And we'll take a picture of those crystals and put it in our lab manual for her and Ulysses to review later. Let's get started!"
2. Have the students bend the pipe cleaner into a shape - snowflakes, hearts, initials - any of those will do. Just make sure it will fit through the opening of the jar.
3. Next, attach their creation to the pencil. You can swing the end of the pipe cleaner over it or use a bit of string, but basically, you want the pencil to be able to rest on the edge of your jar without having your shape touch the sides or bottom of the jar.
4. (***Adults Only***) Now, add hot water until it almost fills the jar, noting how many cups of water it takes to fill the jar.
5. Then, have the students add the Borax - one tablespoon at a time - and stir the solution really well before adding another so that the Borax dissolves. Keep going until no more Borax dissolves - this will be about 3 tablespoons of Borax for every cup of water you have added.
6. Finally, hang the pipe-cleaner-creation in the jar so that it is completely covered by the liquid. Allow the jar to sit undisturbed overnight.
7. The next morning the students should see some crystals growing in the jar. Have them take a picture or draw one on the demonstration sheet found on LM pg. 130 or in their journal.

Results and Explanation

The students should see that crystals formed on the pipe cleaner. If you leave the jar to sit undisturbed for several more days, even more crystals will form.

The Mayo and More

Coordinating Activities

- Art (Solution Painting) - Have the students paint with crystal solution that evaporates leaving behind snowflake-like crystals on LM pg. 131 or in their journal. You will need epsom salts, warm water, a glass, food coloring (blue is best), a paintbrush. You can find directions for this in the following article:
  - https://elementalscience.com/blogs/science-activities/how-to-paint-crystal-snowflakes-epsom-salts
- Snack (Mixture Sandwich and Solution Drinks) - For lunch, have a mixture and solution meal. Make a mixture of your favorite solids in sandwich form and stir up your favorite solution to serve as a drink alongside.
- Activity (Color Mixing) - Have the students mix up several solutions of colored water. You will need 6 cups, water, and eyedropper, and food coloring. Give the students the cups and have them fill three of those cups halfway with water. Have them add several drops of red food coloring to one of the cups with water. Have them repeat the process with yellow and blue food coloring. Then, have them use the eyedropper to add a bit of red water and yellow water into one of the empty cups to make a new solution. What color did they make? Have them repeat the process, mixing solutions of red and blue and of yellow and green, in the remaining empty cups. glass each of red, blue, and yellow colored water on the table in front of you.

Listen While You Eat

Reading Assignment

- *DK Children's Encyclopedia* pg. 168 (Mixtures)

Book Suggestions

- *What's the Solution (Reading Essentials Discovering Science)* by Karen Lewitt Dunn
- *Mixing and Separating (Changing Materials)* by Chris Oxlade

Week 4 Notes

UNIT 8: ENERGY

Unit 8 At-A-Glance

Unit Purpose

This unit is your student's first look at the world of physics. In this unit, the students will learn several basic types of energy and about magnets.

Energy Topics

- ✓ Week 1: Forces
- ✓ Week 2: Sound
- ✓ Week 3: Light
- ✓ Week 4: Magnets

Supplies Needed

Week	Hands-on Project Materials	Coordinating Activity Supplies
1	Toy car, String (2 feet long), Tape	Paint, Marble, Plastic wrap, Several books, Cutting board, Different kinds of round fruits and vegetables, Several rubber bands, Measuring tape
2	An empty yogurt container, Wax paper, Rubber band, Salt, Sound makers (such as a radio, metal pot lid and a wooden spoon, etc.)	2 Paper plates, Paint, Tape, Beans, Rice Krispies cereal, Bowl, Milk, Toilet paper tube
3	A room with no windows, Pencil	Red, yellow, and blue paint, Paintbrush, Different colors of fruit, Flashlights
4	String, Magnet (bar or horseshoe), Variety of metal and non-metal objects	Paper, Thin cardboard, Paint, Several magnetic objects, Sugar cookie, Red and blue M&M's, Magnet

Week 1 Grid Schedule

Main Idea	
A force is a push or a pull that can cause motion or slow it down.	
Supplies Needed	
Hands-on Projects	Toy car, String (2 feet long), Tape
Coordinating Activities	Paint, Marble, Plastic wrap, Several books, Cutting board, Different kinds of round fruits and vegetables, Several rubber bands, Measuring tape

Weekly Schedule

	Day 1	Day 2	Day 3	Day 4
Lunch Items	❑ Make the force science sandwich - read the meat, discuss the bread, and color the page.*	❑ Add some cheese to your sandwich with the hands-on project: Push and Pull.*	❑ Read the *DK Children's Encyclopedia* pg. 108.	❑ Add some mayo to your sandwich with the coordinating activity: Motion Painting.
Feast Fillers	❑ Choose one or more of the library books to read.	❑ Add some more flavor with the coordinating activity: Food in Motion.	❑ Add some more spice with the coordinating activity: Energy Race.	❑ Choose one or more of the library books to read.

** If you are short on time, this item will create a Bare-Bones Snack for your week.*

Week 1 List Schedule

Weekly Overview

Focus-of-the-Week

- A force is a push or a pull that can cause motion or slow it down.

Supplies Needed

	Hands-on Project Materials
Hands-on Project Materials	Toy car, String (2 feet long), Tape
Coordinating Activity Supplies	Paint, Marble, Plastic wrap, Several books, Cutting board, Different kinds of round fruits and vegetables, Several rubber bands, Measuring tape

Weekly Checklist

Bare-Bones Snack

- ❑ Make the force science sandwich - read the meat, discuss the bread, and color the page.
- ❑ Add some cheese to your sandwich with the hands-on project: Push and Pull.

Complete the Lunch

- ❑ Add some mayo to your sandwich with the coordinating activity: Motion Painting.
- ❑ Read the *DK Children's Encyclopedia* pg. 108.

Making it a Feast

- ❑ Add some more spice with the coordinating activity: Energy Race.
- ❑ Add some more flavor with the coordinating activity: Food in Motion.
- ❑ Choose one or more of the library books to read.

Week 1: Forces

The Science Sandwich

The Meat

Read the following introduction to the students (LM pg. 134, RN pg. 62):

Ulysses and I were outside one sunny afternoon having a picnic with our friends, who also happen to be teachers in a local school. I had prepared a delicious chicken salad, complete with almonds and a pinch of paprika – no celery or grapes for this gal!

Anywhoo, I had stuffed those French bread rolls so full of chicken salad that as soon as you picked one up and took a bite, a clump of the delicious concoction fell out the bottom.

And this action led to a discussion of forces with our friends, but before I share about that, what do you know about forces? (Pause to give time for the students to answer.)

Interesting! You see, our sandwiches had no chicken salad motion on our plates. But as soon as we brought them up to our mouths, the force of gravity pulled a clump of the chicken salad from our sandwich down to the plate.

Every day, we encounter forces. These pushes and pulls cause motion or slow it down. Some of these forces we can see, like when we push a car or pull an object toward us. When we make a paper airplane and throw it into the air, the force of our push helps it to fly.

Some of these forces are invisible, like gravity, which pulls objects down toward the Earth, or friction, which slows an object down. We'll chat about another invisible force, magnetism, in a few weeks.

For now, I want you to remember that forces are pushes and pulls that transfer energy. And with that, it's your turn to practice using forces. First, make a paper airplane and then apply a push force to fly your creation.

The Bread

Discussion Questions

- ☐ Ask the students the following questions:
  - ? What is a force?
  - ? Can you name an invisible force that acts on us?

Written Assignments

- ☐ Have the students color the coloring page found on LM pg. 135.
- ☐ Have the students add what they have learned to the force notes mini-book on RN pg. 63. Then, have them glue the mini-book into their journal.

Cheesy Additions

Scientific Demonstration – Push and Pull

In this demonstration project, you and the students will use a push force and a pull force to move a car.

Materials Needed

- ✓ Toy car
- ✓ String (2 feet long)
- ✓ Tape

Steps to Complete

1. Gather up the supplies needed to begin this project.
2. Say to the students, "Summer has asked us to play with force to put a car in motion. We will be using both a push and a pull to see how this affects the toy car. Then, we'll record our findings in our lab manual for Summer and Ulysses to review later. Let's begin!"
3. Place the toy car on the table in front of the students. Ask the students:
   ? Is the car moving or standing still?
4. Have the students push the car gently. Ask the students:
   ? What happened to the car this time?
5. Have the students tape the string to the front of the car. Have them hold the other end and pull gently. Ask the students:
   ? What happened to the car this time?
6. Let the students continue to use forces, pushes and pulls, to move the car around the table. When they are done, have the students write the observations on the demonstration sheet on LM pg. 136 or to their journal.

Results and Explanation

The students should see the car stood still until a force was applied. The push force caused the car to move and so did the pull force from the string. The car continues to move until the force of friction slows it down.

The Mayo and More

Coordinating Activities

✂ Art (Motion Painting) – Have the students paint a picture using motion. You will need paint, a marble, plastic wrap and a book or two. Use the books to prop up the student lab manual and place the plastic wrap under the books to catch the marble in case you don't. Have the students dip a marble into the paint then place it at the top of the activity sheet on LM pg. 137 and let go. Have your student repeat until their paper is covered with tracks of the marble.

- ✂ Snack (Food in Motion) - Have the students play with their food to learn about motion! Have them roll different fruits and vegetables, such as carrots, blueberries, oranges, grapes, or other round food items, down a cutting board ramp to see which rolls the farthest.
- ✂ Activity (Energy Race) - Have the students compete to see who can use the most force to move to their rubber band. You will need several people, a rubber band for each person, and a measuring tape. Draw a line at one end of a room or outside. Give each player a rubber band and have them stand on the line. Call out "pull," at which point the players will us a pull force stretch their rubber bands. Then, call out "let go," at which point the players will let go and the pull force will cause the rubber band to fly forward. Measure the distance each rubber band has traveled. The player whose rubber band has traveled the farthest wins the race!

Listen while you eat

Reading Assignment

- *DK Children's Encyclopedia* pg. 108 (Forces)

Book Suggestions

- *Ways Things Move (First Step Nonfiction)* by Robin Nelson
- *Energy in Motion (Rookie Read-About Science)* by Melissa Stewart
- *Move It!: Motion, Forces and You (Primary Physical Science)* by Adrienne Mason and Claudia Davila
- *Forces & Motion (Little Science Stars)* by Clint Twist

Week 1 Notes

Week 2 Grid Schedule

Main Idea	
Sound waves are vibrations that can travel through the air.	
Supplies Needed	
Hands-on Projects	An empty yogurt container, Wax paper, Rubber band, Salt, Sound makers (such as a radio, metal pot lid and a wooden spoon, etc.)
Coordinating Activities	2 Paper plates, Paint, Tape, Beans, Rice Krispies cereal, Bowl, Milk, Toilet paper tube

Weekly Schedule				
	Day 1	**Day 2**	**Day 3**	**Day 4**
Lunch Items	❑ Make the sound science sandwich - read the meat, discuss the bread, and color the page.*	❑ Add some cheese to your sandwich with the hands-on project: Tonoscope.*	❑ Read the *DK Children's Encyclopedia* pg. 235.	❑ Add some mayo to your sandwich with the coordinating activity: Plate Shakers.
Feast Fillers	❑ Choose one or more of the library books to read.	❑ Add some more flavor with the coordinating activity: Krispie Sounds.	❑ Add some more spice with the coordinating activity: Sound Hunt.	❑ Choose one or more of the library books to read.

** If you are short on time, these items will create a Bare-Bones Snack for your week.*

Week 2 List Schedule

Weekly Overview

Focus-of-the-Week

- Sound waves are vibrations that can travel through the air.

Supplies Needed

	Hands-on Project Materials
Hands-on Project Materials	An empty yogurt container, Wax paper, Rubber band, Salt, Sound makers (such as a radio, metal pot lid and a wooden spoon, etc.)
Coordinating Activity Supplies	2 Paper plates, Paint, Tape, Beans, Rice Krispies cereal, Bowl, Milk, Toilet paper tube

Weekly Checklist

Bare-Bones Snack

- ❑ Make the sound science sandwich - read the meat, discuss the bread, and color the page.
- ❑ Add some cheese to your sandwich with the hands-on project: Tonoscope.

Complete the Lunch

- ❑ Add some mayo to your sandwich with the coordinating activity: Plate Shakers.
- ❑ Read the *DK Children's Encyclopedia* pg. 235.

Making it a Feast

- ❑ Add some more spice with the coordinating activity: Sound Hunt.
- ❑ Add some more flavor with the coordinating activity: Krispie Sounds.
- ❑ Choose one or more of the library books to read.

Week 2: Sound

The Science Sandwich

The Meat

Read the following introduction to the students (LM pg. 138, RN pg. 64):

We have a friend and family member who loves Flamin' Hot Cheetos. He loves them so much that he eats them out of the bag, dips them in ranch, and adds them to his peanut butter sandwich.

I have to say, it's not a sandwich that I want to try – I prefer jelly on peanut butter sandwiches. But it is one of the few sandwiches I know of that makes an amazing sound.

And sound is exactly what we are going to chat about today. But before I share, can you tell me what you know about sound? (Pause to give time for the students to answer.)

Wow! I bet you can make some super silly sounds and we'll do just that in a few moments. The sounds we hear are actually vibrations, or waves, that travel through the air. When those waves reach us, our ears collect them and send the vibration-information to our brain. Our brains interpret that info into the sounds we hear. It's quite the amazing process!

Sound waves can travel through the air, through solids, and through liquids, but the speed at which they travel can change depending on what the vibrations are moving through. That's why it sounds so weird when you try to talk to each other under the water!

The faster the sound waves move, the higher the pitch, or tone, sounds. And the closer the origination of the vibrations is to us, the louder the sound seems.

In short, sound is the movement of energy through something. Now that you understand a bit more about what sound is, it's your turn to make some noise. With your parent's or leader's permission, use your voice, hands, or feet to make some vibrations!

The Bread

Discussion Questions

- ☐ Ask the students the following questions:
  - ? What is sound?
  - ? How do we hear?
  - ? What can sound move through?

Written Assignments

- ☐ Have the students color the coloring page found on LM pg. 139.
- ☐ Have the students add what they have learned to the sound notes mini-book on RN pg. 65. Then, have them glue the mini-book into their journal.

Cheesy Additions

Scientific Demonstration - Tonoscope

In this demonstration project, you and the students will see sound through a homemade tonoscope.

Materials Needed

- ✓ An empty yogurt container
- ✓ Wax paper
- ✓ Rubber band
- ✓ Salt
- ✓ Sound makers (such as a radio, metal pot lid and a wooden spoon, etc.)

Steps to Complete

1. Say to the students, "Summer has asked us to observe sound vibrations with our eyes using a device we are going to make. It's called a tonoscope. This simple device allows us to see the vibrations that sound makes. We'll make our tonoscope, test it with a few sounds, and then we'll record our findings in our lab manual for Summer and Ulysses to review later. Let's begin!"
2. Begin by placing the wax paper over the top of the empty yogurt container and use the rubber band to secure it in place. (***Note*** *- You want the wax paper to cover the entire opening. It should be snug and taut, but not so tight that it causes distortion of the plastic container.*)
3. Set the covered container on a flat surface and have the students gently add about a teaspoon of salt to the wax paper. Shake the container a bit so that the salt lies in one smooth layer that covers the top.
4. Next, have the students make noise near the tonoscope using a radio or by banging a metal pot lid with a wooden spoon. What happens to the salt?
5. When the students are doing this, have them take a picture of the tonoscope and record their observations on the demonstration sheet found on LM pg. 140 or on a chart you draw in their journal.

Results and Explanation

The students should see the salt bounced and moved when sound was made near it. This is because the sound waves produced caused the solid salt particles to vibrate as the waves moved through.

The Mayo and More

Coordinating Activities

- Art (Plate Shakers) - Have the students make a sound producer using two paper plates, paint, tape, and beans. Have your student decorate the bottom of two paper plates by painting the picture of their choice. Then, put several beans on one of the plates. Flip the other plate over and place it on top. Use the tape to secure the two plates together and take a picture to glue on the activity sheet on LM pg. 141. Finally, let the students shake and enjoy!
- Snack (Krispie Sounds) - Have the students observe the sound Rice Krispies can make. You will need Rice Krispies cereal, a bowl, milk, and a toilet paper tube. Pour a bowl of Rice Krispies and milk for the students. Have them listen to the bowl. Then, have the place the toilet paper tube up to their ear and place the other end near the bowl of cereal. Can they hear the cereal better now? Once they are done listening, have them eat and enjoy the cereal.
- Activity (Sound Hunt) - Have the students go on a sound hunt. Head outside and find a good place to sit and listen. Allow your student to observe all the different sounds they hear in nature. You can also try to identify what is making the sounds as you sit and listen.

Listen While You Eat

Reading Assignment

- *DK Children's Encyclopedia* pg. 235 (Sound)

Book Suggestions

- *Sound Waves (Energy in Action)* by Ian F. Mahaney
- *Oscar and the Bat: A Book About Sound (Start with Science)* by Geoff Waring
- *Sounds All Around (Let's-Read-and-Find... Science 1)* by Wendy Pfeffer and Holly Keller
- *All about Sound (Rookie Read-About Science)* by Lisa Trumbauer

Week 2 Notes

Week 3 Grid Schedule

Main Idea				
Light is energy that bounces off objects so that we can see them.				
Supplies Needed				
Hands-on Projects	A room with no windows, Pencil			
Coordinating Activities	Red, yellow, and blue paint, Paintbrush, Different colors of fruit, Flashlights			
Weekly Schedule				
	Day 1	**Day 2**	**Day 3**	**Day 4**
Lunch Items	❑ Make the light science sandwich - read the meat, discuss the bread, and color the page.*	❑ Add some cheese to your sandwich with the hands-on project: Light and Dark.*	❑ Read the *DK Children's Encyclopedia* pg. 147.	❑ Add some mayo to your sandwich with the coordinating activity: Color Wheel.
Feast Fillers	❑ Choose one or more of the library books to read.	❑ Add some more flavor with the coordinating activity: Eat the Rainbow.	❑ Add some more spice with the coordinating activity: Flashlight Tag.	❑ Choose one or more of the library books to read.

** If you are short on time, these items will create a Bare-Bones Snack for your week.*

Week 3 List Schedule

Weekly Overview

Focus-of-the-Week

- Light is energy that bounces off objects so that we can see them.

Supplies Needed

	Hands-on Project Materials
Hands-on Project Materials	A room with no windows, Pencil
Coordinating Activity Supplies	Red, yellow, and blue paint, Paintbrush, Different colors of fruit, Flashlights

Weekly Checklist

Bare-Bones Snack

- ❑ Make the light sandwich - read the meat, discuss the bread, and color the page.
- ❑ Add some cheese to your sandwich with the hands-on project: Light and Dark.

Complete the Lunch

- ❑ Add some mayo to your sandwich with the coordinating activity: Color Wheel.
- ❑ Read the *DK Children's Encyclopedia* pg. 147.

Making it a Feast

- ❑ Add some more spice with the coordinating activity: Flashlight Tag.
- ❑ Add some more flavor with the coordinating activity: Eat the Rainbow.
- ❑ Choose one or more of the library books to read.

Week 3: Light

The Science Sandwich

The Meat

Read the following introduction to the students (LM pg. 142, RN pg. 66):

Glow-in-the-dark sandwiches – good idea or bad idea? One April Fool's Day, a McDonald's in India put out a meme with a glow-in-the-dark hamburger. It looked interesting, but very unappetizing.

Turns out, it was a gimmick and wasn't a real sandwich they were offering. Food doesn't make its own light; instead, light helps us to see those sandwiches on our plate.

But before I go into more about what light is, let's take a moment so you can share what you know about light. (Pause to give time for the students to answer.)

Ahh, you never fail to surprise me! Light is basically energy. It's energy that bounces off of objects to that we can see them. Our eyes take in all that bouncing energy and send the information to our brainy parts. And our brains turn that info into the pictures we see.

The light can be split into different waves that represent the different colors of the rainbow. You know those right? (Pause) Right, Roy G. Biv – red, orange, yellow, green, blue, indigo, and violet. And this fact allows us to see different colors.

The sun is our greatest source of natural light, but we can also get light from candles, electronics, light bulbs, and stuff that glows-in-the-dark. Remember, when we block out the sun, or any other light source, we can create a shadow. This is a dark area when that takes the shape of the object that is blocking out the light!

Now it's your turn. Can you make a few shadow puppets on the way using your hands and a flashlight?

The Bread

Discussion Questions

- ☐ Ask the students the following questions:
  - ? What is light?
  - ? What are the colors of the rainbow?
  - ? Name a source of light.

Written Assignment

- ☐ Have the students color the coloring page found on LM pg. 143.

- ☐ Have the students add what they have learned to the light notes mini-book on RN pg. 67. Then, have them glue the mini-book into their journal.

Cheesy Additions

Scientific Demonstration - Light and Dark

In this demonstration project, you and the students will see how light helps us to see the objects around us.

Materials Needed

- ✓ A room with no windows
- ✓ Pencil

Steps to Complete

1. Say to the students, "Today, Summer has asked us to explore how a room looks with and without light. We'll observe the with the light on and with the light off and then we'll record our observations in our lab manual for Summer and Ulysses to review later. Let's get started!"
2. Have the students go into a room with no windows with you. Have the students describe what they see.
3. Then, turn the lights off and have the students describe what they see now. (***Note** - If you have a student that is afraid of the dark, allow them to have a very small flashlight.*)
4. Turn the lights back on and have the students draw what, or list the objects, they saw when the lights were on and when they were off on the demonstration sheet on LM pg. 144 or in their journal.

Results and Explanation

The students should see that when the lights were on in the room, they were able to see all of the objects. They should also see that when the lights were off in the room, they were not able to see any of the objects.

The Mayo and More

Coordinating Activities

- ✂ Art (Color Mixing) - Have the students make their own color wheel. You will need red, yellow, and blue paint, and a paintbrush. Have them begin by painting red, yellow, and blue in the marked sections on the activity sheet on LM pg. 145 or in their journal. (*Be sure that the students paint thickly, as they will use the extra paint in the next step.*) Then, have the students drag a bit of the red color and a bit of the blue color into the empty section and mix the two colors together to make purple. Repeat this process to make green and orange.

- ✂ SNACK (EAT THE RAINBOW) - Choose a fruit for each of the main six colors of the rainbow and serve them for snack. For example, you could serve strawberries, orange slices, bananas, kiwi slices, blueberries, and grapes.
- ✂ ACTIVITY (FLASHLIGHT TAG) - Have the students play a game of flashlight tag. See directions for this game here:
  - https://lifestyle.howstuffworks.com/crafts/home-crafts/easy-outdoor-team-games-for-kids5.htm

LISTEN WHILE YOU EAT

READING ASSIGNMENT

- *DK Children's Encyclopedia* pg. 147 (Light)

BOOK SUGGESTIONS

- *Light Is All Around Us (Let's-Read-and-Find-Out Science 2)* by Wendy Pfeffer and Paul Meisel
- *All About Light (Rookie Read-About Science)* by Lisa Trumbauer
- *The Magic School Bus: Gets A Bright Idea, The: A Book About Light* by Nancy White
- *All the Colors of the Rainbow (Rookie Read-About Science)* by Allan Fowler

Week 3 Notes

Week 4 Grid Schedule

Main Idea	
Magnets are attracted to certain kinds of metal.	
Supplies Needed*	
Hands-on Projects	String, Magnet (bar or horseshoe), Variety of metal and non-metal objects
Coordinating Activities	Paper, Thin cardboard, Paint, Several magnetic objects, Sugar cookie, Red and blue M&M's, Magnet
	*(***Note*** *- You will also need two bar magnets for the science sandwich.*)

Weekly Schedule				
	Day 1	**Day 2**	**Day 3**	**Day 4**
Lunch Items	❑ Make the magnets science sandwich - read the meat, discuss the bread, and color the page.*	❑ Add some cheese to your sandwich with the hands-on project: Magnetic Attraction.*	❑ Read the *DK Children's Encyclopedia* pg. 151.	❑ Add some mayo to your sandwich with the coordinating activity: Magnetic Art.
Feast Fillers	❑ Choose one or more of the library books to read.	❑ Add some more flavor with the coordinating activity: Magnet Cookies.	❑ Add some more spice with the coordinating activity: Magnetic Hunt.	❑ Choose one or more of the library books to read.

** If you are short on time, these items will create a Bare-Bones Snack for your week.*

Week 4 List Schedule

Weekly Overview

Focus-of-the-Week

- Magnets are attracted to certain kinds of metal.

Supplies Needed*

	Hands-on Project Materials
Hands-on Project Materials	String, Magnet (bar or horseshoe), Variety of metal and non-metal objects
Coordinating Activity Supplies	Paper, Thin cardboard, Paint, Several magnetic objects, Sugar cookie, Red and blue M&M's, Magnet

*(***Note*** *- You will also need two bar magnets for the science sandwich.*)

Weekly Checklist

Bare-Bones Snack

- ❑ Make the magnet science sandwich - read the meat, discuss the bread, and color the page.
- ❑ Add some cheese to your sandwich with the hands-on project: Magnetic Attraction.

Complete the Lunch

- ❑ Add some mayo to your sandwich with the coordinating activity: Magnetic Art.
- ❑ Read the *DK Children's Encyclopedia* pg. 151.

Making it a Feast

- ❑ Add some more spice with the coordinating activity: Magnetic Hunt.
- ❑ Add some more flavor with the coordinating activity: Magnet Cookies.
- ❑ Choose one or more of the library books to read.

Week 4: Magnets

The Science Sandwich

The Meat

(***Note*** *- For this introduction, you will need two bar magnets.*) Read the following introduction to the students (LM pg. 146, RN pg. 68):

I am a sandwich magnet, which, by now, you have probably already guessed. I always manage to find a new sandwich to try in every new place we visit, and I am rarely disappointed.

After all, is there a better meal delivery system than a sandwich? I think not. But we are not here to discuss the culinary merits of sandwiches.

We are here to discuss our last science sandwich together . . . sniff, sniff . . . this one is all about magnets. But before I share, what do you know about magnets? (Pause to give time for the students to answer.)

Ahhh-mazing! I have so enjoyed your answers this year, and I will miss our little chats!! Magnets like to attract things, such as metal stuff and other magnets. The area around a magnet where it can attract things is called a magnetic field. Some materials are naturally magnetic, and some can be magnetized, meaning that we give them the properties of a magnet.

Either way all magnets have two sides, which we call poles. Just like on the Earth, a magnet has a north pole at one end and a south pole at the other. If you put two magnets together, a north pole will attract a south pole, while a north pole will repel, or push away, another north pole.

Now it's your turn. I want you to get two bar magnets – those are the long, bar-like ones – and play with them. Try sticking them together and try to get them to repel each other!

The Bread

Discussion Questions

- ☐ Ask the students the following questions:
  - ? What does a magnet do?
  - ? What do all magnets have?

Written Assignment

- ☐ Have the students color the coloring page found on LM pg. 147.

- [ ] Have the students add what they have learned to the magnets notes mini-book on RN pg. 69. Then, have them glue the mini-book into their journal.

Cheesy Additions

Scientific Demonstration - Magnetic Attraction

In this demonstration project, you and the students will see what magnets are attracted to and what they are not attracted to.

Materials Needed

- ✓ String
- ✓ Magnet (bar or horseshoe)
- ✓ Variety of metal and non-metal objects

Steps to Complete

1. Say to the students, "Today, Summer has asked us to play with magnets. We know from her introduction that magnets are attracted to certain metals. So, today we have a variety of objects to test to see if they are attracted to a magnet. Then, we'll record our findings in our lab manual for Summer and Ulysses to review later. Let's get started!"
2. Lay the objects out on the table.
3. Have the students use a magnet to try to attract the objects. Let them observe what objects can be picked up by the magnets and which ones cannot.
4. Have them add their observations to the demonstration sheet on LM pg. 148 or in their journal.

Results and Explanation

The students should see that some objects were attracted to the magnet and some objects were not affected at all by the magnet.

The Mayo and More

Coordinating Activities

- ✂ Art (Magnetic Art) - Collect several magnetic objects, such as a metal washer, a metal ball, and a paper clip, for the student to paint with. Use a piece of paper taped onto a thin sheet of cardboard to give the paper some strength. Have the students dip the metal objects in paint and then put it on the paper. Use a magnet from the underside of the paper to drag the object across the paper so that it "paints" on the paper. When they are done, let the paper dry and then attach it to LM pg. 149 or in their journal.
- ✂ Snack (Magnet Cookies) - Make your favorite sugar cookie recipe. Use red and blue M&M's to make the design of a magnet on the cookies. Bake and enjoy.

✂ ACTIVITY (MAGNETIC HUNT) - Give the students a magnet and let them walk around your house or outside in the yard testing various objects to see if they are magnetic. (***Note** – If you let them test inside the house, be sure not to let them use the magnets near computers or other electronic devices.*)

LISTEN WHILE YOU EAT

READING ASSIGNMENT

- *DK Children's Encyclopedia* pg. 151 (Magnets)

BOOK SUGGESTIONS

- *Magnets (All Aboard Science Reader)* by Anne Schreiber and Adrian C. Sinnott
- *What Makes a Magnet? (Let's-Read-and-Find... Science 2)* by Franklyn M. Branley and True Kelley
- *Magnets: Pulling Together, Pushing Apart (Amazing Science)* by Natalie M. Boyd

Week 4 Notes

SUMMER'S LAB

APPENDIX

Frog Life Cycle Pictures

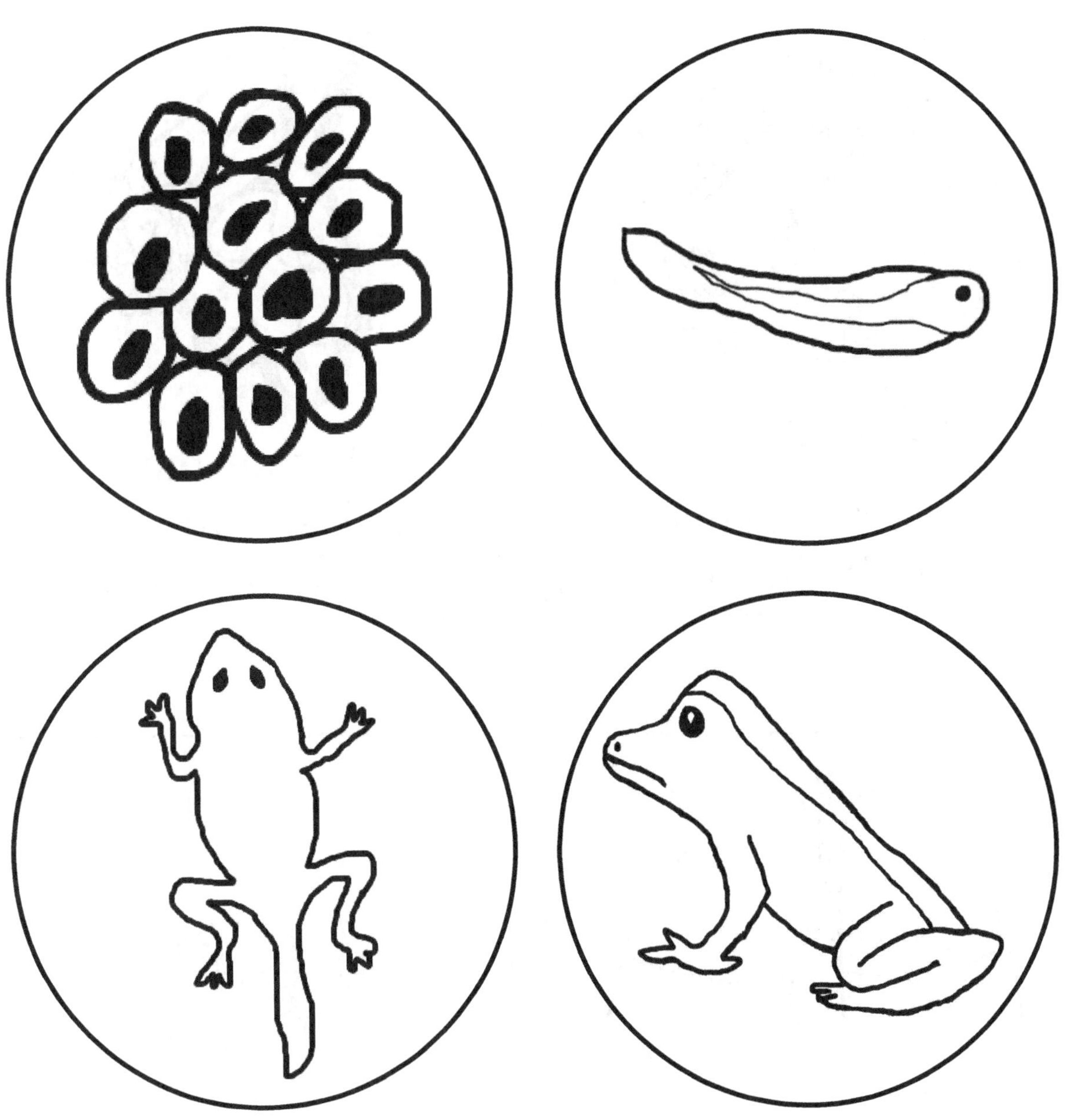

Body Organiztion Cards

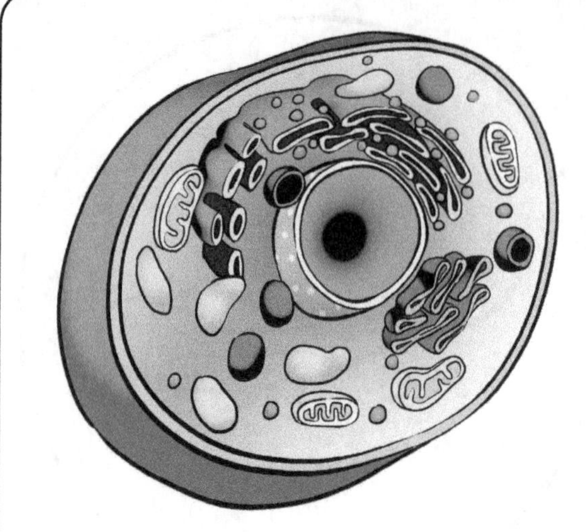

Cells are the smallest living units in the body.

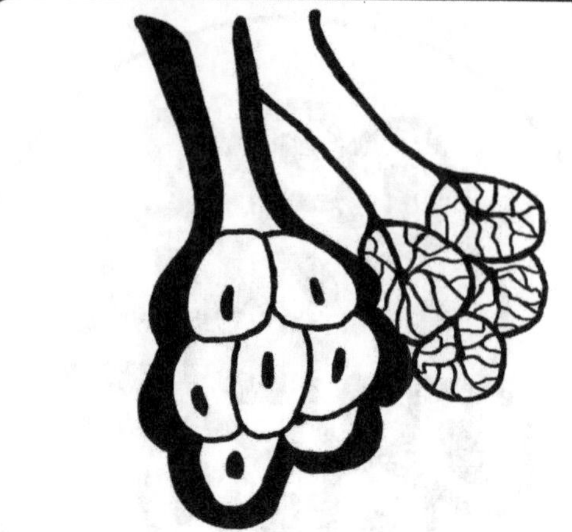

Cells that have the same job join together to form tissues.

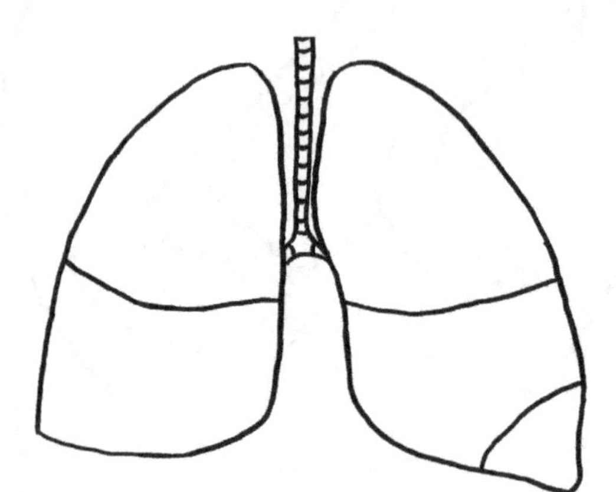

Several different types of tissues work together to make an organ.

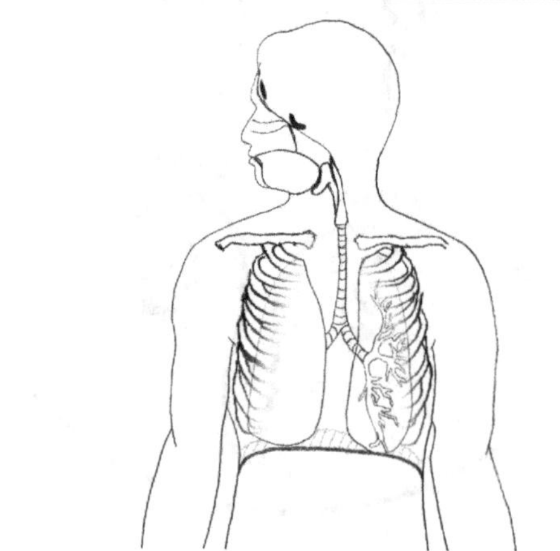

Organs work together in a system to perform the functions of the body.

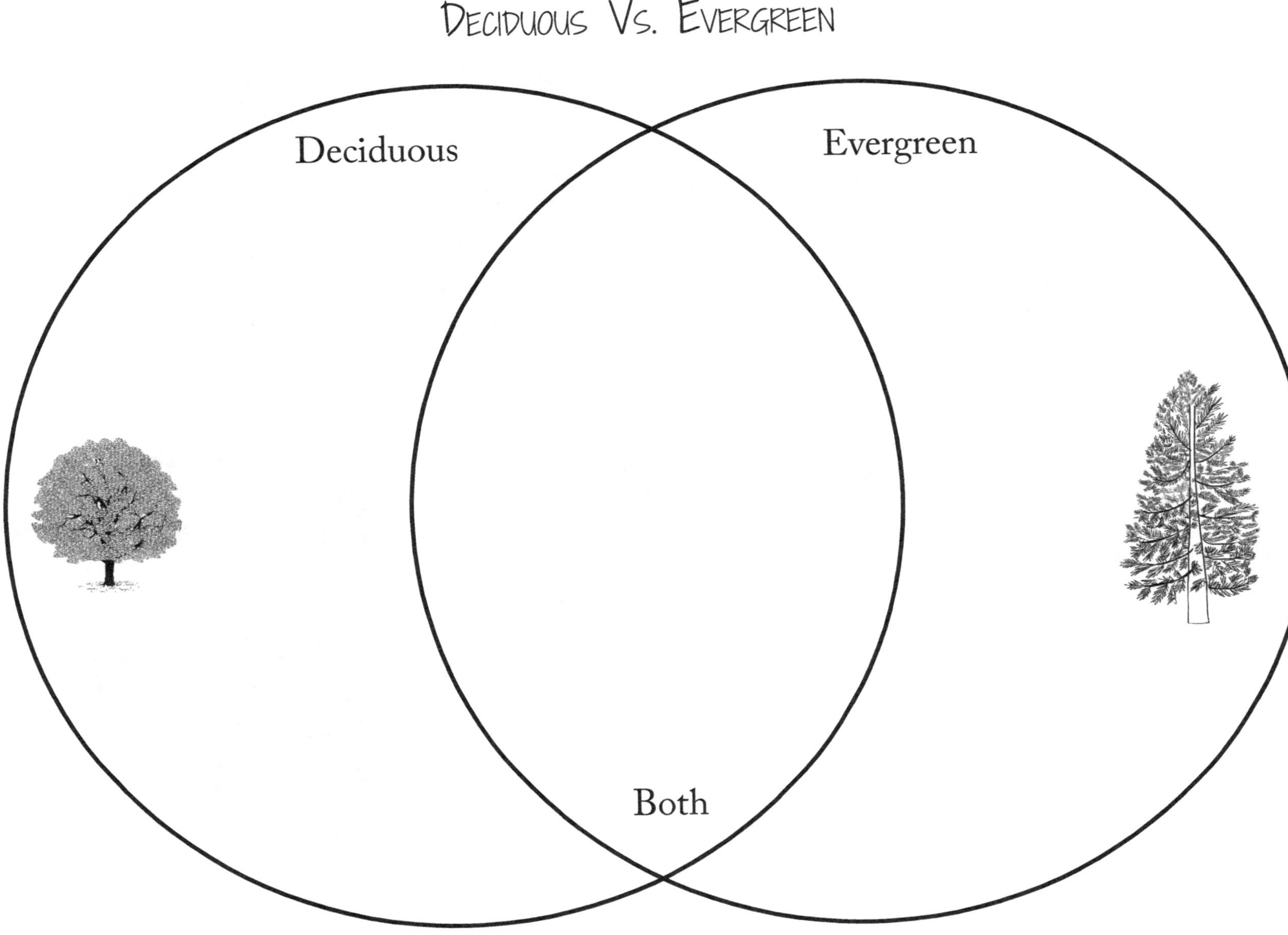
Deciduous Vs. Evergreen
Deciduous
Evergreen
Both

Cloud Matching Templates

Weather Stickers

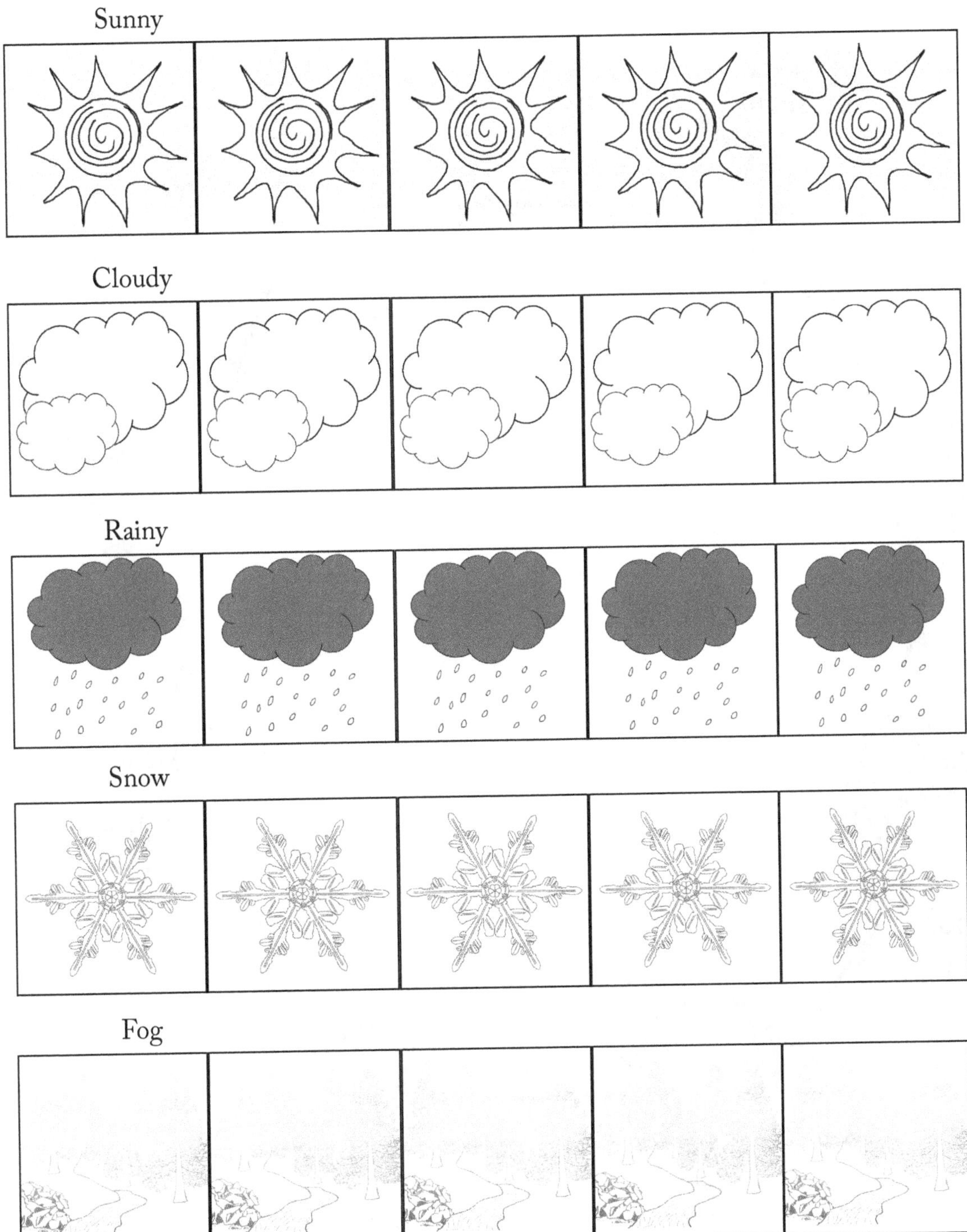

Phases of the Moon

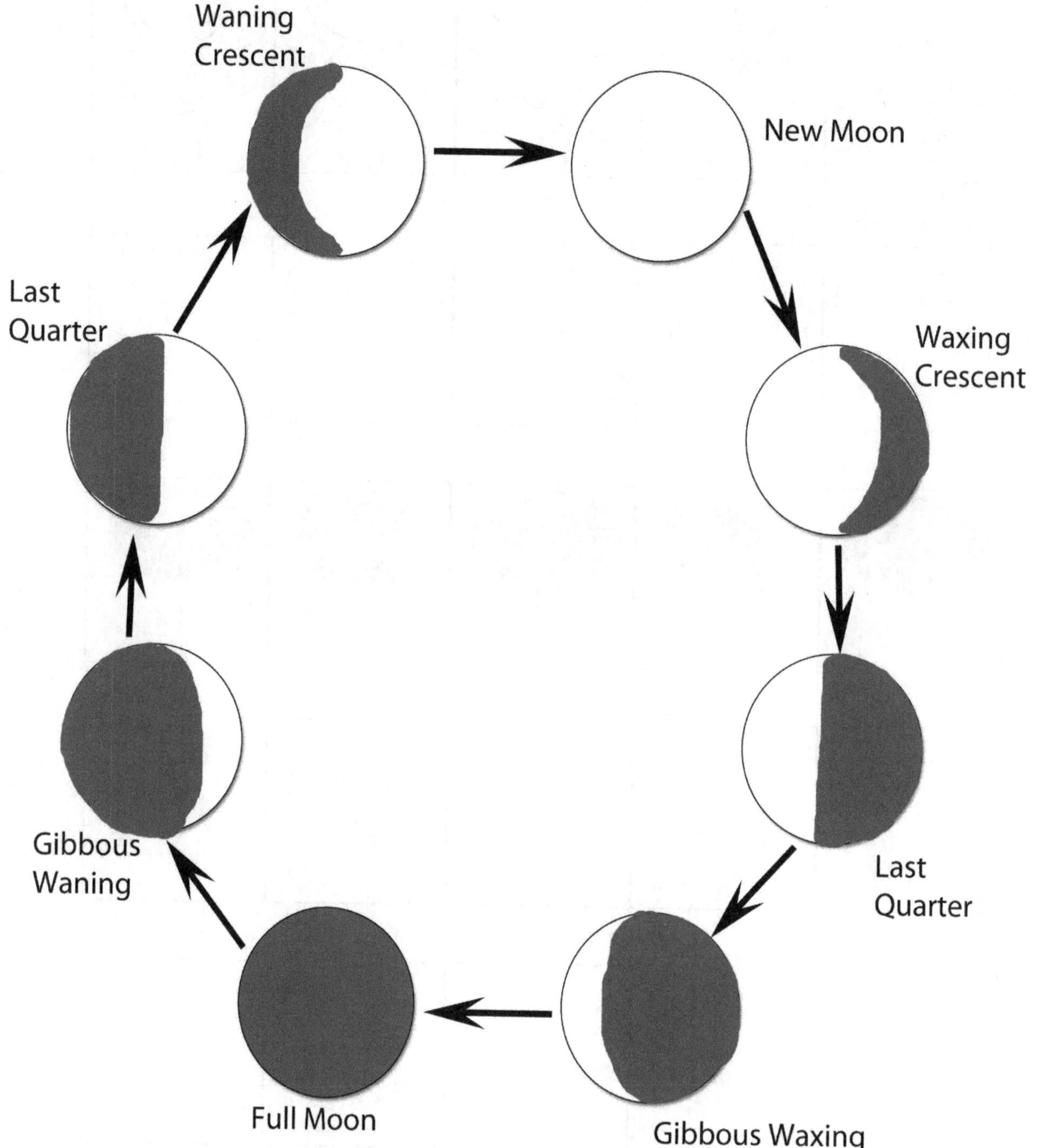

Solar System Labels

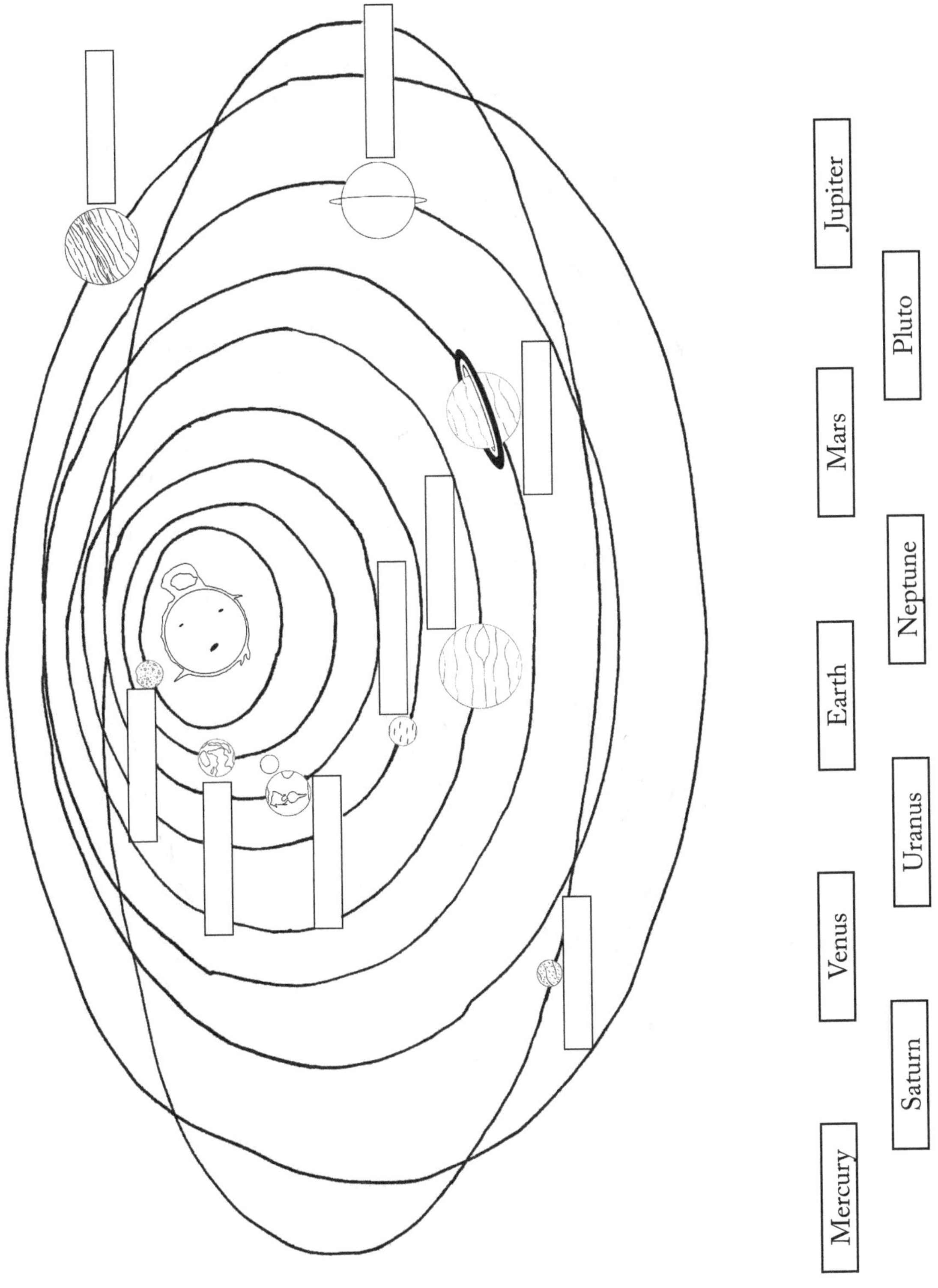

Labeled Solar System

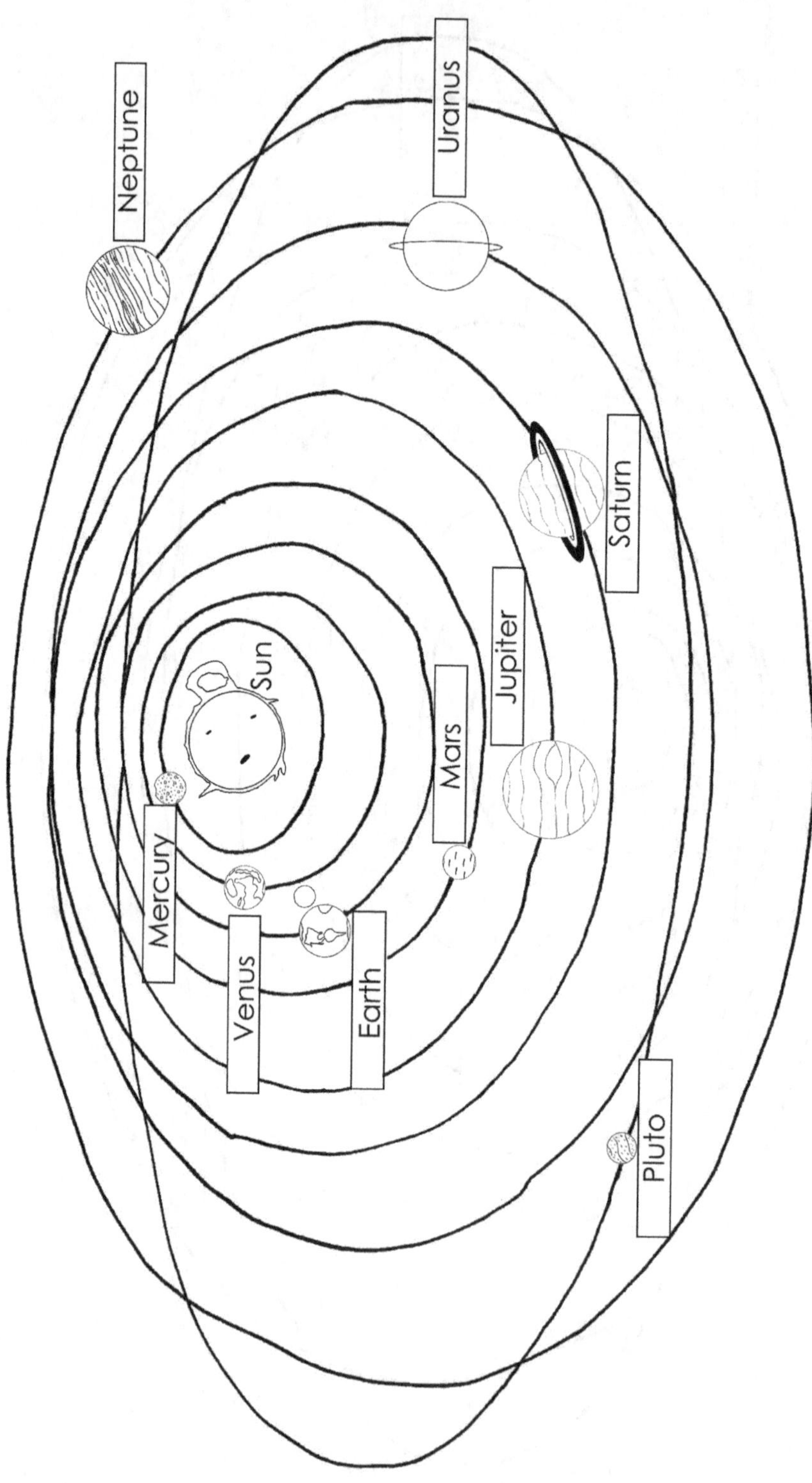

Constellation Templates

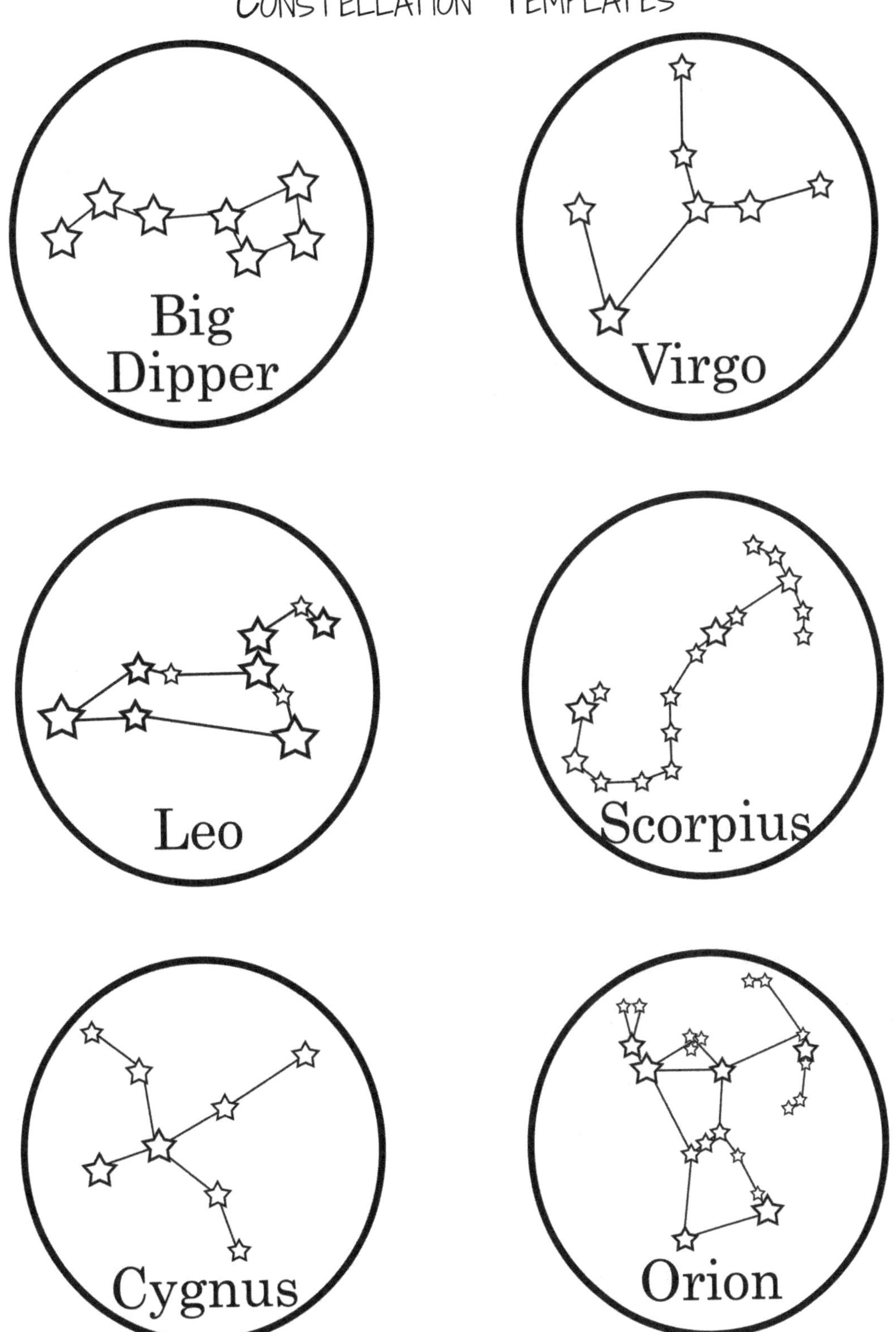

Made in USA - Kendallville, IN
1129496_9781935614715
06.30.2020 0945